From the ...

... to the Clyde

Jenny Robertson

Fleming Publications

ISBN: 978-0-9556507-8-9

Cover design: Etta Dunn

Top cover photograph: "Black devils" (Soviet marines) landing on Volga banks. Autumn 1942
Courtesy of Volgograd Archives

Bottom photograph Copyright © Etta Dunn 2014
Sunset over the River Clyde

Fleming Publications
Fleming House
Glasgow

Contents

Polish soldiers playing with Wojtek
Courtesy of Mirror Features

Introduction

"It is necessary to remember," says Karol in the story called *The Apple* but in Poland where these war time stories are set, memory is fraught with complexities. Because the effects of the Second Word War were so total, historians of this relatively recent past have to act as archaeologists, so a piece of ephemera, an apple, a wooden flute, a mezuzah become signposts to vanished events.

These stories are worked from personal memories passed on to me when I lived in Warsaw. Freyde came from a Yiddish song and the story, exactly as narrated here, provoked a memory from Danuta, the story of her father's lost love. The story of the apple and the story of the mezuzah were given to me by Joanna. Karol, the guardian of memory was a neighbour in Warsaw. The story of the birthday present was told to me by a colleague. She didn't tell me exactly where her father had lived in Poland so I set the story in the lost Borderlands. The River was sparked by an episode in a Polish newspaper, along with meeting elderly people, impoverished and frail who, sixty years before, had risked their lives to rescue Jewish people. The Israeli ambassador awarded them the medal Righteous Among the Nations. I read the story of the children's home in the archives of the Jewish Historical Institute in Warsaw. I took no notes, the facts seared themselves into my memory and are told in the true story of the little boy-god, the boy-fighter and the girl who had been buried alive.

The grandmother whose secret I narrate was a close friend and I did indeed discover her secret act of heroism when I was travelling on a bus from Aberdeen. Two friends in Edinburgh kindly gave me their grandfather's stories; the German grandfather's story is based on the memoirs of Mr Herbert Sachse and the Russian story comes from Zapiski Komandira Strelkovogo Bataliona by Mikhail Shelkov. Wojtek the bear leapt out at me (as Wojtek always does!) from an open-air exhibition in Warsaw.

There is nothing invented in these stories but the knowledge around them is the fruit of years of study. I became involved with Polish war trauma when I worked as a student volunteer in displaced persons' camps in Germany which led me to study Polish. I spent a post-graduate year in Communist Warsaw and more recently lived and worked in independent Poland, where I collected the memories retold in this book.

The Apple

S he was in the autumn of her life, but her skin had a sheen which hinted at youthful good looks. Old Karol, watching from his ground-floor window, was reminded (and he was quite a connoisseur) of an apple a little past its sell-by date, but crisp around the core.

Karol lived in Hay Street, right beside the one remaining fragment of the wall that had surrounded the Warsaw Ghetto. As a youngster Karol had watched the red brick wall rise ever higher. He had seen boys his age, or younger, carry bricks for their own prison. When the war and destruction was over new buildings began to rise on rubble and bones and the ghetto wall became a silent ghost. Karol decided to commemorate those thousands turned to ash.

He fixed a map of the whole ghetto area to the wall and put up a plaque, explaining what had happened there. Then he created a little garden, shut off by a low swing gate. As the years went on Karol, self-appointed guardian of memory, planted flowers and bushes in the little garden and kept an eye open for visitors to his shrine.

The woman had hesitated outside the gate, pushed it open and walked slowly up the path towards the wall. She pulled off her gloves and unfastened her coat. It was warm in the shelter of the wall. Karol opened his back door and crossed his own garden with remarkable agility.

"Good morning, Madam."

She swung around, startled. His blue eyes were friendly and his open manner invited confidences. She let him seat her on a wooden bench with her back to the red brick edifice. They chatted of this and that while traffic roared by on the other side of the wall and the city got on with its normal business of living.

Their talk turned to her girlhood. There was something she wanted to say, but she found it hard to begin. She shifted position on the wooden bench, crossed and uncrossed her legs —nicely shaped, Karol noted with approval. She lifted her crinkled hand to her mouth. Her nails were painted faintly pink.

"I'll never forget it," she began.

Karol waited.

"A little girl, you know, sent away to Granny in the country to be safe. It was autumn, so sunny and warm. Granny sent me to the farm for milk. She gave me an apple in case I felt thirsty on the way."

She paused; again her hand went up to her mouth, covering her thin lips.

"I had to cross the railway line. A train had stopped just ahead of me, a long line of closed goods trucks and all along the wagons little things fluttered like flags. But they weren't flags. They were hands, lots and lots of little hands, fingers jerking up and down like puppets dancing. Children's hands...and voices crying, 'Mummy! Let us out... help... water!' That's what they shouted most—water. Only it wasn't really shouting, just a kind of animal howling from inside those sealed trucks."

She paused. Her faded eyes misted, looked deeply within.

"I pulled my apple out of my pocket. It was so red and shiny, so good to eat. I ran up to the train, right close up. I had to stretch up really high. I pressed the apple into one of the hands. It was probably a boy's hand. The boys would be the strong ones, wouldn't they? They'd be the ones who would force their way through the crush to get close to the cracks to get air. The boy took the apple, his fingers curled round it just as the train jerked and started to move away.

"But he couldn't pull the apple inside. The crack was too narrow, large enough for his hand to go through, but not wide enough for the apple. I hadn't thought about that, hadn't thought that the apple would be too big. The train started up. It gave a big jerk and pulled away. I watched it go with all those little hands waving like flags and one of them holding my apple and struggling, struggling to get it through the crack."

She fell silent and Karol waited. They had plenty of time. It was pleasant here, sheltered by the wall.

"I'll never forget it. It haunts me, the child's hand holding the apple, his very last apple, and me standing there, so helpless. I suppose he dropped it, just opened his fingers and let it fall. It would have been better not to have given the apple at all. It just made it worse for him. I shouldn't have done it. It wasn't right..."

Karol pressed her hand. "Dear lady, when everything is wrong, can anything be right? Would you like to take a closer look at the wall?"

She looked around her as if she'd only just noticed the wall, the garden and Karol himself, "The wall? Oh yes."

They stood up. Karol led her closer to the wall.

"This is all that's left of the Warsaw ghetto wall," he explained.

She pointed to the map. "And you did this... and made the garden too?"

"It is necessary to remember," Karol said.

She nodded. "Do many people visit the wall?"

"Very many. Some take pictures, others light candles or lay stones or formal wreaths—but you, madam, have brought your story."

He bent over her hand, raised it to his lips and kissed it. The red brick wall towered above them, while, beyond the wall, trams rattled over their tracks like departing trains.

Freyde, my Freyde

Her name means joy. Joy, sweetness, oh yes! The sweetness of first love, the joy of being with my Freyde. A lifelong joy for a short-lived sweetness, a lifelong song for a long lost love.

I shall never forget that summer day on Honey Street in Warsaw.

I heard her before I saw her; she sang as she walked. Love notes, joy notes, all the wonderful delight of living, even though it was high summer and the pavements were melting in the heat. People with money went away for the summer. Young people with less money went to summer camps, but others, poor like ourselves, stayed in town.

Freyde, you brought me the sweetness of summer with your song!

So, I turned to see who it was who sang.

She seemed at ease with herself. Her clothes were neat and simple, her eyes, dark pools of peace—and her hair, her abundant hair! She wore it piled high on her head; its rich hues shot through with amber. She realised that I had overheard her song and she blushed.

"Don't stop! You were singing so beautifully!"

A smile shimmered across her lips. We fell in step and in far too short a time we had arrived on Pleasant Street, her home.

"Please let me see you again."

She hesitated. "School starts soon."

Was that just an excuse? Perhaps so, but I replied with a smile that must have cracked my face in two, "Then we must meet sooner than soon! Tomorrow at eleven?"

She didn't make any promises. I heard her light footsteps as she ran up wooden stairs, where, so soon, heavily booted feet would tramp. I turned away—and I realised that I still did not know her name.

Before eleven next morning I stood outside her house, half expecting that she would not appear, but she came on time. Her thick plaits were coiled like a crown above her brow.

"My name is Freyde," was her answer to my query. The words sang in my ears after her voice had died away.

We met again and again those late summer days. Freyde was seventeen, and I was just a year older. She wanted to study music. I wanted to be a doctor. But these were distant dreams. There were shadows of war on the horizon and already in parks and gardens the leaves on the horse chestnuts were turning gold.

On the last day of the holidays we caught a train out of town. We walked through forests lit with a fretwork of sunbeams. Together we picked wild strawberries: summer's sweet juice stained our lips.

There in the woods we shared our first kiss, sweeter than wild ripe fruit. We stood back, trembling, and all the bright trees seemed on fire around us. But the fire was within us; after all these years I remember that flame.

Soon, all about us, other fires blazed. Destruction fell from September skies. I did not see Freyde, but I dreamt of her. As nights brought fresh terror I wondered if she lay awake, afraid. I longed to comfort her, to loosen her dark hair and bury my face in that thick softness, as though that might release magic which could lead my princess to safety.

Months went by. We were harassed, mocked, ill-treated, and imprisoned behind high walls. The bitter winter cold saw our people standing in long queues in snowy streets, queuing for food, for permits for this, for that, for everything: queuing, it seemed for the right even to live.

Soon we would be queuing to die.

I could have escaped. My brothers found a way out but how could I leave my Freyde?

Bombed out buildings sheltered beggars, and everywhere reeked of the stench of sickness and decay. That was when I saw Freyde again, standing in line for food.

Our eyes met. Her hands flew to her head. I clenched my fists. Hunger and sickness had forced her to crop her hair.

11

She turned away from me, like a child who thinks she is hidden because she does not see.

I called her name but a great tumult of desperate people closed around her. That night I recalled my foolish fancies. I remembered the thick hair shot with amber I had longed to unbind and fondle. I cried for Freyde's hair, for the magic I had deluded myself might have saved her from misery.

I tried to find out where she lived, but no one knew. People were moved from street to street, from room to room. New people kept arriving; hundreds died. We were always hungry, always cold; hopeless, yet frightened to die, though death was on every corner of every street.

Then, against all hope, I met Freyde again, bending over an old woman who had collapsed in the snow. Together we carried the woman into an unlit basement and laid her on sodden straw. There were others there, many more, old, sick, despairing, but what could we do? They had this poor shelter at least; others, young and old, starved in the streets. We shut the door. Then we turned to each other.

Everything I wanted to say died on my lips.

"Can it be true?"

She nodded, looked away, "It's the end of everything."

"No, Freyde, not for us. We're young. We'll survive. I love you, Freyde."

Her eyes filled with tears, "You can't say that here."

"I love you," I insisted. "It's better than food to see you."

"Forget me," she said. "It's better not to remember."

"Have you forgotten me, Freyde, forgotten those summer days and the taste of wild berries?"

"That was then. That was the dream. We've woken up now."

"How can you say such a thing?"

"Don't you know?" She was crying now. "Do you really not know?"

"Tell me," I put my arms round her. This time she clung to me. I slid my fingers across the poor stubble of her hair.

"They're coming!" she cried. Footsteps rang out on the frozen pavement. Booted men marched towards us. Freyde's hands flew to her lips. She ran away. I cowered back against the doorway, but they caught me, knocked me around, then let me go.

It didn't matter. Nothing mattered until I could see Freyde again. I wanted to comfort her, to make her hope.

Can you hope in the ghetto?

Some people found escape in music. The miseries of the ghetto produced new songs, and there were always those who sang, and those who gathered around to listen, but my sweet singer was never there. High summer came and the merciless deportations began. I found Freyde among other fugitives, rigid with fear in a frail hiding place.

We clung together, breathing the quick, trapped breath of the hunted.

When the roundup was over we crept, trembling, outside into the August sun. Freyde said, her voice choked with grief, "I've lost my mother and my little sister. I came into that hide-out to look for them. I don't know where they've gone."

I drew her to me. Crying together for our love and our hurt we lay in the shadows of the ghetto and comforted each other with our loving. Freyde sighed, cuddled close to me, "How I should like to sleep now, and waken beside you to find that the nightmare is over."

I stroked her hair. It curled around her head, soft and dark and gleaming like amber. "The nightmare will end one day, Freyde, and we'll lie together in a soft bed under a goose feather quilt."

She shivered. "Mother's ill. She needs me. And Pola's only eight. People say we are all being sent further east to work. To work... when you are only eight years old? When you are sick? No, no, I've got to find them."

She fastened her ill-fitting dress. I stooped and held her shoes steady while she stepped into them.

We never saw each other again.

Day in, day out, I have learnt to understand and mispronounce languages which are not my own; but never can I forget Freyde's summer song in the lost language of our love.

I live on and grow very old, but my thoughts remain in Warsaw. My spirit circles above that rebuilt city, searching for the girl whose dark hair was shot through with amber, searching for Freyde.

Footsteps

A group of women sat together around the kitchen table, in a flat in Warsaw, sharing coffee and stories and memories. I told them the story of Freyde and then Danuta shared her father's story.

"When my father was sixteen the love of his life was a Jewish girl called Ciwia, Ciwia Hirsh. See, I even know her name! Ciwia lived in town. My father was a village boy, but they went to the same school.

"Then the war began. Late one evening someone knocked at the door of the cottage in the village where my father lived. It was actually the first house in the village with open countryside on the other side. The knocking wasn't loud, it was very gentle, but just the same, the family just froze. It could have been the police, come to take someone away; but in that case the knock would have been different, loud and persistent. This knock was soft, beseeching; so after a moment's thought, my grandfather opened the door.

"Mr Hirsh, Ciwia's father stood on the doorstep. Grandfather looked all around and invited him in. My father offered the stool he had been sitting on and Mr Hirsh told them that he had walked all the way from town, about fifteen kilometres away. He had avoided roads and even lanes. He was sure no one had seen him come to the door. After all, my father lived in the first house, so he hadn't had to walk right through the village.

"He had come, he said, because of Ciwia. He wondered if my grandfather would take Ciwia in, let her live with them, hide her. They were going to be sent away. They knew that trains went away full and came back empty. So he had walked all that way to my father's village."

Danuta paused. We waited, wondering what would happen next.

"My grandfather refused," Danuta said, "My father was sitting there, and he heard his father say 'no' to Ciwia's father. There were five younger children, you see, and my grandfather had to think of that. He had those five kids to look after – and you know what happened if Poles were caught hiding a Jewish person – even giving a piece of bread, or helping in some way. But it wasn't just the five kids. He reminded Mr Hirsh that their house was the first in the village. That meant they would be the first to be searched. That's what the problem was, the location of the house. And so he said no.

"They didn't turn Ciwia's father away, though. They gave him food. They let him have a rest. Even that was dangerous. Then he went away…"

Danuta paused, "Darkness was falling and the kitchen window filled with cloudy twilight. In the silence, in the half-light, we heard a muffled sound. It was the father who had walked fifteen kilometres. He had rested now. He must go. He stood up, a shadow among the shadows in the cottage. He hadn't wanted to be a trouble. He had just come because… And now he must go. He had a long walk ahead. He turned towards the door. His footsteps made just the slightest, muffled sound on the wooden floor."

One of us asked, "Did anyone survive? Did Ciwia…?"

"How could they survive? There was nowhere else to go. It was because it was the first house in the village, you see, it was too dangerous."

"Yes, if it had been the last one, right beside the forest…"

Our talk had shut out the sound of footsteps crossing the wooden floor but now we listened again. A father was leaving a one-roomed home. A father who had no choice was shaking hands with a father who had made his choice. The father who had no choice steps out into the night. The door shuts behind him; the latch is dropped with barely a sound.

The doomed father doesn't have to linger in the village. The house is the first one, right at the very edge. Just a few metres to go and he will have left the village safely behind him. Perhaps he had frowned upon his daughter's friendship with a Polish boy. Perhaps though, as the noose pulled ever tighter, his wife had said, "But, Moshe, that's the very thing which could save her life. The boy loves her. Go and ask them to take her in."

So he went... and now he is returning and the answer is, "No."

But Ciwia lived on in her young lover's helpless heart. That first love was never forgotten. His daughter actually knows her name, all these years later. And Danuta added, "My own mother wanted children so she took my father in. She made room in her house, her bed, her body, for a man she didn't love for the sake of the children she wanted to have. And if she hadn't, I wouldn't be here. But for the lost love, the girl his father would not save, my father never made room in his heart for anyone."

Now we hear them clearly, the footsteps retreating into the night. Those footsteps have been walking unceasingly for seven long decades. They walked into the room where we sat, a small group of women under the darkening sky. And when we parted, the footsteps followed us home.

Those footsteps walk across Poland, across Lithuania, Latvia, Ukraine. Their muffled tread leads into the forests of Belarus, they traverse the by-ways of Europe. Other steps join them, and more, and more. Listen: they are walking into the darkness, those footsteps of a people for whom all roads were closed.

Inside the Sewing Machine Drawer

After we had heard Danuta's story about her father's long lost love, our little group of women decided to meet more often to tell these stories of memories which had impacted on our lives. Joanna ran a small café devoted to Jewish things, musical events, art exhibitions, poetry readings and so on. She had set up a small display case.

"It's a memory store. I wanted to gather small, everyday objects from a vanished world, ordinary things that have become extraordinary because the people who owned them have vanished from the earth. Like this, for instance…"

She showed us a curved metal object, a container of some sort.

"It's a mezuzah case," Joanna explained. "It would have been fastened to the right side of the front door— mezuzah means *doorpost*. It contained a scroll with words from the Torah. Most Jewish homes in Poland had one and you can sometimes see the marks on the woodwork of pre-war buildings that show you that this house had once belonged to a Jewish family."

Then she told us her story.

She had received a letter from a small town in western Poland, a rambling letter, with uncertain punctuation from a woman called Maria Grabowska.

"I heard about you on the radio. Mother and I were repatriated from the east at the end of the war. We had to pack up in a hurry, but she managed to take her sewing machine. She put it in a handcart along with whatever food she could get hold of, bundles of bedding, pots and pans. She put my little brother on top. I walked alongside with a rucksack across my shoulders – I was almost seven. Mother trundled that cart along to the train. I'd never been in a train before, but I can tell you, it wasn't exactly luxury: we travelled in a cattle truck. The journey took three weeks. Do you know how we survived? Some people in our truck had brought their cow. Every time we stopped, which we did quite a lot because the train kept getting checked—they pushed the cow out to graze, and we all got busy scraping out the evidence of the cow from our truck. But we had milk, straight from the cow.

"You may be wondering, what's all this got to do with the sewing machine? Well, inside the sewing machine drawer Mother had put a small metal object. I don't know exactly what it is, but it's something Jewish. Mother felt that it must be important because the lady who gave it to her asked her to look after it carefully. So Mother tucked it away inside her sewing machine drawer. She kept hoping the people it belonged to would come back and claim it, but no one ever came, and when Mother passed away I didn't want to throw it away either. But now I'm getting on and my kids for sure will just chuck it away. 'That old metal thing, there's no use keeping that,' they'll say. They'll chuck the sewing machine out too. 'Old-fashioned,' they'll say. 'You can buy electric ones nowadays.' But I don't want to break faith with something my mother promised so long ago, so I decided I would write to see if you could advise me what to do..."

Joanna told us she had written back and had offered to make the long journey across to western Poland to see Mrs Grabowska. But then it turned out that Maria Grabowska had to visit her sister-in-law in Warsaw, so it was decided that she would call in herself with this souvenir from another time, another place.

She had arrived, breathless with haste and apologies, a small stout woman with patchy face powder, reddened lips and greying hair escaping from a severe looking hat. Joanna helped her hang up her coat and ushered her towards a table beside the display case. Maria took off her hat and pulled out a powder compact to survey her flattened hair.

"Oh dear me, I'm so sorry I'm so late. I never thought it would take so long."

"Well, you've come a long way. Never mind, you're here now. Tea? Or coffee? Or perhaps something cold?"

"Tea, please."

She was rummaging in her bag and pulled out a crumpled plastic bag which she unwound with much rustling.

"Here it is, the thing my mother kept so carefully for so many, many years…"

She laid the small, oblong piece of metal on the white tablecloth.

"A mezuzah case!"

"Is it? Jewish families used to have them at the entrance to their homes, didn't they? I think I can remember them from the small town where I grew up, but I'm not sure. It was so long ago. Mother said some people touched it as they entered or left the home, but she didn't know why. Kind of like a holy water stoup, but of course it wouldn't be, would it, holy water, I mean?"

"No, but," said Joanna, almost mechanically, "may I have a closer look?"

"Of course, of course, that's why I brought it. Here," Maria pushed the mezuzah container across the cloth and Joanna cradled it carefully in her hand.

"So," she said slowly, "this is what your mother kept in her sewing machine."

"That's right, tucked away inside the little drawer. I used to love that drawer when I was small. I'd always be pulling it in and out and peeking inside."

"Do you remember what happened? You said someone gave it to your mother?"

"That's right. It was Mrs Goldfarb. She was the doctor's wife."

"And where was this? Where did you live?"

"Oh, you won't have heard of it. It was a small town near Lwów. Of course, that's in Ukraine now."

"But in those days…"

"Oh, a right mixture," Mrs Grabowska stirred sugar into her tea. "Poles, Ukrainians, Jews, Armenians, two or three Czech families too. The Goldfarbs were Jewish, of course. My mother used to do dressmaking for the family and sometimes I'd go along to the house with them. They had a nice, big house. Of course I have only the vaguest memories. Sometimes I seem to see a house with a feel of space and, oh I don't know, comfort maybe, and sometimes I think it's just because Mother has told me about it and I can't really remember at all.

"But when the war began, the Russians came, and then in 1941 the Germans... I was only four but I remember it quite clearly. You know, they show films about the war nowadays, but I never watch. I remember soldiers with big boots and guns and harsh faces—and motor bikes. To this day the sound of a motor bike makes me feel as though I'm standing at the edge of a big black pit... horrible."

"Horrible indeed," Joanna agreed.

Maria Grabowska sipped her tea. "That's how it was for the Jews. They wiped them out. But three years later they came for us too, all sorts of bandits. They call it ethnic cleansing now. However, by the time we were repatriated, as they called it, sent off in those cattle trucks to western Poland, the war was over and there were no Jews left in our little town—none at all. And there had been a synagogue and kosher shops and a school for the boys. A cheder it was called. It was just one small room, which opened off the street. We used to go past the cheder on our way to market and see the boys all with their caps on crowded together reciting long passages of the Scriptures off by heart in Hebrew. Some were no bigger than I was then, three or four. Imagine killing little boys and their teachers just because they studied the Bible! It's the same God after all, isn't it? At any rate, that's what they say now when it's too late—when they've all disappeared. They didn't say it then, but my mother did and she brought me up like that, you know."

"Is that why Mrs Goldfarb gave your mother the mezuzah case?"

"Perhaps. I've never really thought about it. She came and knocked at our door. Mother opened it, and it was Mrs Goldfarb. She was in a big hurry. She said, 'I've come to say goodbye. We're going away, but we don't know where to—

nor for how long. We have to be ready by noon'.' "

Maria's blue eyes filled with tears. She searched in her bag for a handkerchief, blew her nose and continued.

"You can imagine what a good person Mrs Goldfarb was if she still found time to rush out and say goodbye to her neighbours."

"She'd obviously brought the mezuzah case with her, which must have meant she knew…"

"She knew. And yet she didn't know. She told Mother something about going into the forests.

'Perhaps they want us to fell trees,' she'd said, 'but the elderly, the children?' And there had been no mention of where they were supposed to live. Perhaps, too, she hadn't anything valuable left. The Russians had stripped their home, you know, because they were that bit better off and lived in a bigger house… They made the Goldfarbs live in one room and quartered soldiers in the rest of the house. And when they went away they took Mrs Goldfarb's silver and her nice table linen, my mother said. But then the Germans came and they took all the Jews away. And we were left with this…"

Her gaze went across to the mezuzah case which Joanna had laid back down on the table. But the scene replayed across the old woman's inner eye had taken place a lifetime – a death-time ago. And Joanna saw it too: two women standing in a low-ceilinged room. Sunlight filtered through the leaves of yellowing lime and poplar trees and fell in patches on the earthen path outside the little wooden house. A slight breeze rustled the leaves. It was a golden autumn day with just a hint of chill but Mrs Goldfarb wore a felt hat, a thick coat with a warm jacket underneath and several layers of clothes under that; and on her stockinged feet were sturdy shoes.

"My husband's father built our home," she said. "I came here as a bride. My children were born here. And now it's time to leave."

"Your husband delivered my babies, little Darek and darling Maria."

"She's a credit to you. We love it when she comes round. Came, I should say."

And then there was silence. Maria said that she had never forgotten the way that the golden autumn day had become anxious, tense. A dog barked, a deep-throated bark from the jowls of a brute trained to kill. A motor cycle roared through the sleepy square of a little town and Mrs Goldfarb bit her lip, half turning towards the door.

"I must go…"

Perhaps the Polish seamstress had said warmly, "Go well, dear Mrs Goldfarb, you and your family. I'll keep this safely for you until we meet again."

But whatever she had said, she had kept faith, and so had her daughter after her. They had kept the mezuzah case. It lay on the white tablecloth, a small piece of decorated metal from another time, another place and yet now for all time and for every place.

Joanna looked at it again. "Thank you for bringing this to us, Mrs Grabowska, and thank you for sharing the story. I shall be proud to display this for you—and for Mrs Goldfarb and her family."

"Oh, yes, please. I'm glad I brought it to you. It would have been terrible to have thrown it away. It's a little act of memory, isn't it, that means the dear Goldfarb family haven't been forgotten."

"That's what it's all about," said Joanna.

She helped Maria with her coat and saw her out.

"So that's the story of the mezuzah case," she told us and she gave it to us to hold.

How many other hands had touched this metal after it had been nailed in place on the door-frame of the Goldfarb's home? And what had Mrs Goldfarb done with the precious parchment when she had unscrewed its container?

"So many unanswered questions!" Joanna sighed, putting the mezuzah case back into her display cabinet. "The Rabi of Kobryń has said, *Only when you possess knowledge do you know what you were lacking.*"

She smiled and left us to think this through. Maria Grabowska and her mother had known neither the name nor the purpose of the object they had kept so carefully. Nor had the Goldfarbs known what awaited them in the forest from which they had never returned.

The mezuzah case, emptied of the scroll with its eternal command, but preserved in a Polish woman's sewing machine drawer, had kept faith beyond the mass grave and the slow drift of leaves falling from thick clustered trees. And now it rested behind glass, dumb witness of the time when the noise of shooting had ceased, the last motorcyclist had roared away and the little town had been pronounced racially clean.

His Excellency, the Holy One

Two young women stood face to face in an unlit room. "Take him, please keep him safe for me," Dora begged. Afterwards all that Krysia would remember were her eyes, bottomless pools of fear and sorrow, resolution and pain. Krysia would see those eyes again and again as she looked at Dora's child; bottomless pools, also, but innocent of fear or pain. He would look up at her with his mother's eyes and she would remember...

"Yes, I'll take him," Krysia bent over to take the bundle in Dora's arms. "He's beautiful."

The young mother seemed not to hear. "Afterwards, when it's all over, you will give him back, won't you?"

Krysia nodded, but she had the child now.

"There's money too, gold, my wedding ring."

Krysia didn't want to hear. "Go now, go, it's too dangerous."

"Yes, I'll go. Please, just one more look." Dora edged forward. The hostile look she saw in the other woman's eyes made her drop her hand. "Yes, I'll go. You're right. It's too dangerous. Thank you, thank you."

"It's nothing. I've always wanted a child."

Dora caught her breath. She wanted to say, *so did I. I love him more than my own life and now I've given him away. Be worthy of my trust, of my great gift.* But she was the debtor. She turned away.

* * *

For the next eight months Krysia looked after little Tadek (as she called him) as if he were her own. She gave up her job in the corner shop to care for him, trusting her savings and Dora's bundle of money and gold would keep her and the baby. Her parents might have helped out with food from their allotment, but she couldn't tell them about Tadek. She could not hurt them with a double lie, pretend that this was their grandchild and scandalise them with the shame of an out-of-wedlock infant. All right, it was war-time and things happened, but all the same… So she rented a room in a place where she was unknown and took in washing, pushing Tadek in a dilapidated pram to pick up dirty linen, carrying it back the same way through the war-torn city. She tried to slip the other woman's wedding ring over her swollen fingers, but it was too small, and anyway she needed the money it fetched when she sold it at a fraction of its value. She had no cot, so she took the child into her own bed and doted on him day and night, this baby with eyes which spoke to her of the mother whose place she had taken.

Her secret hope was that Dora would never return— but this was too wicked a thought. Only as she pushed the pram around the bombed out streets, alert for blackmailers who might tip off the powers-that-be, she spun thoughts in her head, that yes, Dora would return, but would not want her baby back. *You have looked after him so well, he belongs to you now,* Krysia would hear Dora say. Or perhaps the mother would come back safely but not be able to locate the son whose eyes lit up when Krysia chattered to him above the steaming wash-tub. He had cried at first, for two or three days, but that was long ago and now she was the only mother Tadek had ever known. Or did some memory lurk deep within that little mind, diamond bright, of a mother who had not needed to wash other people's clothes?

The problem came when Tadek was almost a year old. He was hard work now, crawling everywhere, getting into everything. He was gregarious, a little prince… a contrast to the dowdy woman who pushed his pram, who clearly wasn't his mother, yet couldn't be his nanny, because what would a nanny be doing in this run-down street, carting bundles of washing in her pram? The concierge dropped remarks as Krysia crossed the courtyard. Neighbours went into a huddle as she passed—she felt their stares. And still her little prince drew all the looks of passers-by. Wreathed in smiles, he doted on adulation and seemed to attract the adoration of every person who came his way. His smile was graciously bestowed, munificent: he was the one to whom the world paid court. Grannies stopped to talk. Total strangers smiled. Then one day as Krysia bumped the laden pram over broken paving stones, the boy who sold cigarettes on the pavement—a dangerous, illegal trade, tipped her a wink. "Better be careful, missus. It sticks out a mile."

She stopped in her tracks, trembling. "I'd get rid of that kid before they turn you in," the boy went on. She nodded, groped in her bag for a coin.

"You didn't see me... you don't know a thing," she stammered.

He pocketed the coin. "It's a deal."

Could she trust him? Probably not, but perhaps it would buy her a moment's space. Her throat was dry. Her knees shook as she turned back home. She sensed neighbours' stares and tried to pretend she hadn't seen their knowing looks.

Krysia lived on the fourth floor and the lift seldom worked. It would have been easier to take her bundle of washing first, leaving Tadek strapped in his pram below. But she could never do that: the risks were too high, so she always carried Tadek up, settled him in her room, closed the door and went back downstairs for the load and then finally for the pram. This time was no exception—but she found the neighbour from along the corridor blocking her way. She was a big woman, fond of the bottle. She was one of the few who remained oblivious to Tadek's smiles.

"Excuse me..." Krysia began, but the woman cut her short. "That brat's one of *them*. Get rid of him, you'll get us all shot."

Krysia nodded dumbly and to her relief the woman edged away and she could unlock the door.

She sat down, holding Tadek, both still fully dressed in their winter clothes.

"Tadek, my little Tadek, my precious one, my own."

No, that was the problem, he was not her own. She rocked him in her arms, but he was restless, over-warm in his layers of clothes. She stood up and went to the window, but immediately drew back afraid that prying eyes might notice her with the child. She put him down. He fussed, but she left him and opened the door a fraction. The neighbour had gone, but that didn't mean that the corridor was trouble-free.

"We'll go for a walk."

She quickly packed a small bag and fitted a teat over a feeding bottle. Tadek took it and sucked contentedly as she carried him back downstairs to the pram. An idea was forming in her mind. Once, pushing her pram with the big bundle of washing balanced on top, she had met another woman, also laden with washing. Drawn like everyone to Tadek's charm, she had soon got chatting to Krysia. "What a gorgeous little boy! You know my cousin belongs to a religious sect, Children of the Rising Sun, they're called. They believe a god will come to earth as a year old boy-child and they'll all be reborn. Takes all sorts! But it's the war, you know, people are ready to believe in anything. They get themselves up in long robes—that's what's in the bundle. It was my cousin's turn to do their washing but she took ill, so muggins here stepped in. Better be careful, they might kidnap your little boy! No, I'm kidding of course! They're pretty cracked but they wouldn't do anyone any harm. Only, he has a sort of Eastern look about him, just what they'd like to have in their god. They meet in that bombed out old meeting hall."

Krysia knew what she must do.

It really was the only way. She found the chapel; a flight of broken steps led to a cellar. She picked her way down, holding Tadek and pushed her shoulders against the makeshift door. It wasn't locked. The place was warm enough; some sort of iron stove pipe in the corner must have been connected to the house next door and gave out heat. There were no windows or seats. Paper flowers decorated an altar before which a little lamp burnt in a jar, too high for Tadek to hurt himself. She put him on the floor with his feeding bottle. His eyes, surprised and reproachful, looked up at her through the gloom. Krysia didn't dare linger. She hurried away, knowing he would start crying for her behind the closed door. She gave up her rented room and went back to her previous address, taking up work once again in the corner shop. Her arms felt empty and her heart was sore.

* * *

The Children of the Rising Sun were overawed when they found an infant divinity, flushed and tear-stained, sleeping in their poor temple.

"The god has visited our war-torn earth!" they whispered. "The oracles have told the truth." They dispersed to spread the glad tidings among the faithful who brought sweetmeats, flowers, honeyed milk to their little god.

And so Tadek lived in the cellar, worshipped and adored. He wore robes stiff with embroidery. Devotees sat with him day and night. They thought it beneath his divine dignity to crawl, so they taught him to sit in the yoga position. Some of his very human behaviour puzzled them somewhat, but they hung upon his childish talk, finding great wisdom in his babble. They named him 'His Excellency the Holy One.' His every word was their command.

Perhaps, they said, *the war will end now that the Holy One is here on earth.*

But it was almost two years more before the war ended and a little longer before the mother who had survived picked her way among ash and rubble searching for her son. Dora looked pinched and famished. She wore a nondescript headscarf, a threadbare coat whose frayed cuffs did not quite conceal the number tattooed on her arm. Krysia's shop was in ruins, the street corner obliterated, but incredibly Dora tracked her down.

"I had to give him away," Krysia confessed, and no, she didn't know if the temple which held the divine child had survived the fires, the shooting and the bombs. It wasn't too far away, on such and such a street…

Amazingly the cellar-temple had survived. Incense smoke filled the room—and there he was, her little son, plump and well-fed, handsome as a little prince, just as Krysia said. Her heart stopped. Had she not stayed alive for

29

this? Devotees surrounded him. Half a dozen white-robed figures clustered around her son—she saw them through a blur. She drew closer and they looked round. They put their hands together and said a word. Her little boy did the same, his eyes twinkling above his folded finger tips.

Dora choked. Tears filled her eyes. She couldn't speak. "The little boy... he's mine. He's my child, Shmuel."

"Shmuel," they repeated, their gentle, ingenuous eyes wide with wonder. "Shmuel."

"He's mine. I want him back."

They looked at one another. A girl spoke up, "Please ma'am, the child is our Excellency, our Holy One."

"Our Excellency, our Holy One," her child repeated. His voice had the same timbre as hers. Dora felt her famished insides contract.

"I've come to take you home, Shmuel."

The child's eyes widened.

"What is home?" His puzzled eyes searched the faces of his faithful followers.

"He is our god," they said, shaking their heads.

"He is my son," Dora said.

There were murmurs; a few tears were shed but no one except Shmuel resisted when Dora tried to take his hand.

"Come to Mummy, Shmuel," she coaxed, but he snatched his hand away. She wanted to pick him up, he stiffened in her arms.

"He has no outdoor clothes," they said, and while someone went out to see what among all the rubble, might be found to fit a well-fed boy of four, Dora knelt beside him and spoke gently to him.

"I had to give you away," she told him, "I wanted to save your life."

She could see that he didn't understand. Tears choked her. "I gave you to a woman called Krysia and she must have brought you here."

"We found him sleeping in front of our altar," some of the faithful explained and told her how they had honoured their Holy One and made him his silken shirts and embroidered robes. Shmuel listened. "Mummy?" he repeated wonderingly, but without affection—and how indeed could he feel affection for this mother he had never known?

He let them put a shabby coat over his embroidered robes, and held out his feet as a woman brought shoes which had belonged to her own child.

"He has never worn shoes," they said and they kissed his feet as they slipped on the unaccustomed footwear.

"Farewell," they said and blew out the candles in front of the small god's throne.

So Shmuel stepped into a world he didn't know. He had not seen daylight since Krysia had pushed him about in his pram. He had never walked outside before. He was fascinated and scared at the same time. The going was rough. He stumbled and fell. He dragged along, a dead weight in Dora's hand.

"Come, Shmuel," she coaxed—but he was the one who gave commands.

"Don't want you," he said.

With sinking heart she could tell she was not going to have an easy time with him. Anger and bitterness rose in her heart. She half pulled, half dragged her son along.

* * *

Shmuel's life had definitely taken a turn for the worse! His mother rented a narrow room in a bombed out building. It had once been a maid's room, opening off the shared kitchen. There were three other rooms split up between four separate households, including a grandmother, mother and two little girls, while the elderly lady who had once owned the whole flat was quartered in a large cupboard.

Everyone had stories of loss and survival; they were all eye-witnesses of things they wished to forget, but with a new occupying force in power, people preferred to keep themselves to themselves. Caution was the key. They all worked long hours, apart from the elderly woman, who tottered round ruined yards, collecting scraps of food, broken bottles, bits of rag which she boiled for hours, stinking out the kitchen and filling it with steam. Dora found a job in a stockroom, only there was no stock. She had to travel two, sometimes three hours on almost non-existent transport: creaking tramcars, so overcrowded that each one was festooned with people clinging to the sides like grapes around a vine, or lorries that broke down more often than they moved. Many parts of the city were without power, roads were blocked or obliterated. It was better to walk, but the going was hard: rubble and ruin, mud or black ice in winter, dust clouds in summer. Everywhere there was the danger of unexploded bombs and landmines. Everywhere too, the work of rebuilding was going on. Children played in the rubble, and the workmen who laid new foundations, dug up bones.

Shmuel was left alone. The little crown prince, once doted on by Krysia, the little god, whose every wish had been a sacred command, was locked into a narrow slip of a room on the fifth floor. He who had never known hunger was growing thin. He who had been surrounded by adoring worshippers, now had to put up with a mother who was never home, or when she did appear, was too tired to do more than wash him and feed him with boring, insufficient food. She had to wait her turn at the single stove, at the single toilet and the single cold water tap. Shmuel wasn't allowed in the kitchen: he got in the way. He contented himself with darting into the hallway when his mother's back was turned, tripping people up and, if he could, sneaking into the room with the two little girls. He pulled faces at them, stole their picture books and once, when they were sitting at the table, drawing with pencils they scrupulously shared, he pulled their pigtails. Their mother and grandmother evicted him and yet another outlet for his pent-up intelligence was closed.

At weekends his mother tried to take him out for walks; once she took him to a puppet play. Shmuel watched entranced. He fed off the memory for weeks. Bored out of his mind, he climbed up on to the window ledge and managed to open a small casement window set into the larger pane. He had no idea of heights or of the law of gravity, and even if he had known they would have made no difference to a divinity who would rule the world one day. But even so, he felt a bit scared as he peered through the open window at the street far below. Nonetheless, he poked his head through the small pane and started to ease his shoulders through. That felt scary, but he enjoyed the feel of the fresh air about him. He watched pigeons fly from rooftops across the yard. Could he fly too? Why not? Yet some innate fear held him back. Halfway in, halfway out of the window he saw people point and shout. That was fun! He waved back.

"Look at me! I'm going to fly down to you."

His voice carried, but not his words, nevertheless, they were alarmed. The next thing he knew a motor-lorry with a clanging bell careered down the street. He watched, too scared and fascinated to move, but then a huge thing came wavering out of the lorry, pointing its two sharp ends towards him. Shmuel wriggled back into the room in alarm and shut the window quick. He sat trembling on the floor out of sight of this great monster that had reached out its arms to grab him.

That evening a neighbour knocked at the door. Dora opened it reluctantly. "Good evening, my dear. My name is Goldblatt. I live across the yard. May I speak to you about your son?"

Dora let her in and hastily pulled her sleeve over the tattooed number on her arm, but Mrs Goldblatt appeared not to notice. She told Dora about the fire engine and added, "I give art lessons in a children's home. It's just a few streets away. There are good people there. Why not enrol your little boy?"

"In a home!" Dora looked shocked. "No way!"

"I know, dear, but you see, you cannot give him the care he needs. The neighbours wanted to take the matter to the Children's Court.'

"No!" Dora screamed and Shmuel started to cry.

"See, he loves me," Dora said, her voice choked.

"You can visit him at weekends. It would be just until you get back on your feet again. Otherwise, you see, they could take him away for good. This way, the decision's yours, he's nearer home, you haven't lost him and you'll be helping him get back to normal life. There," she said to Shmuel. "Look, I've brought a sweetie for you." Shmuel stopped crying and unwrapped that rare treasure while Dora asked about the home. Were they really good people? Did they have a place for her son? Could she really see him at weekends?

"And holidays too," Mrs Goldblatt assured her with much nodding of her close cropped grey head. "I'm on duty tomorrow. Why don't I speak to the lady director? And would you let me take Shmuel along while you're at work so that he can have a look at the place, play with the children?"

"He doesn't know how to play," Dora said, sadly.

"They were all like that. He'll learn."

But the next day Shmuel hid under the sofa-bed and no amount of cajolery, threats or proddings would get him out. Dora, exasperated, despairing, locked the door on her son and went off to work. Let that brat jump out of the window—see how I care... But her mind lurched away from that awful thought. She did care—but he didn't. He wasn't even six and she couldn't control him, the son whose childhood had been snatched from him along with her maternal care.

She asked off work early and went to the home. The Director, Miss Letitia, looked thoughtful but did not refuse her request. "All our children are damaged. Bring Shmuel along tomorrow."

"Suppose he doesn't come?"

"Tell him he's going to meet some new friends," Letitia suggested. "You don't need to bring his clothes—you can call round later with them when he's settled."

"He only has one set of clothes."

"No problem. We have things now—people have been good to us; we had nothing at all when we started."

"How did you get started?" Dora didn't really want to

know—she was groping for an answer to her own problems.

"I went back to the place I'd lived and started walking among the ruins, wondering if I could find any trace of my former life, the little bits of jewellery I'd hidden, or, even more importantly, anyone to call my own. There was nothing and no one, but I found a little huddle of damaged children and a new life's work."

"You just stumbled upon them?"

Letitia replied with a sad smile. "Yes and no—perhaps they stumbled upon me? I saw a Russian soldier leading along—well, something. I couldn't be sure. Not something I recognized, almost like little ragged bundles, but they were too thin and scrawny even to be called bundles. Then I saw that they were children, of my people—and yours too, I think?"

"Are you...?" Dora didn't finish the sentence.

"Yes, I am! So you see, we must rebuild our lives."

"I've been trying..."

"Of course you have, my dear, of course you have, and against many odds! But let's get back to the children. The soldier simply handed them over to me. 'Here, take them, they're yours,' he said. 'Vot, pozhaluista, here, please,' she repeated and in spite of herself Dora smiled.

"The soldier pointed to an empty building," Letitia went on. "There were no panes in the windows, the door was torn from its hinges, but the children—and I—had all known much worse. So we huddled together. They were crawling with lice and had dear knows what kinds of infectious illnesses. Some children couldn't walk properly because they hadn't used their muscles for years. Others were fit—they'd been in the forests with the partisans. They'd been ten year old soldiers, and now they've had to learn to be children."

"My son doesn't know how to be a child either,"

"Bring him to us. The children help one another. They are all damaged. They all carry impossible scars. One little girl was found starving, filthy dirty, beside the decomposing body of her mother, walled up in what had been their hiding place underneath a burning building. She was four years old."

Dora didn't react. She had seen too much. She simply nodded, and Miss Letitia went on, "Our children have all endured too much but we help them live beyond those memories. Our psychologist encourages them to paint and draw. At first they drew soldiers, guns firing, girls and boys running away, dead bodies. They drew little child figures and giants with menacing faces. Then they started to draw happier things—home—they told us about their parents, brothers, sisters and grandparents. They began to encircle these figures with sunshine and rainbows, butterflies and flowers. It's harder for them at day-school. But here in the children's home, there's nothing to hide."

"I'll be happy to bring Shmuel to you. I hope he doesn't throw a tantrum though."

Letitia smiled at that. She stood up and pulled open a drawer.

"Here are some of the children's pictures. Take them home and tell him he can draw and paint nice pictures like this while you're at work."

Dora brought Shmuel the next day. She hated not telling the truth, but she couldn't face his tantrums.

"Shmuel," she said, "it's not been right leaving you locked up alone while I'm at work. I'm going to take you to meet new friends. You'll be able to play with them and see Mummy when she's not at work."

Shmuel stared. He'd been abandoned three times already, once by this mother of his, and once by another woman he'd thought of as his own. And although there had been no mother among the Children of the Rising Sun there had been Dawn and Larksong who festooned him with garlands and taught him how to cut out paper flowers, while Sunrise and New Day, kneeling, served him raisins and sultanas and danced with him to the music of soft flutes. They had made him butterflies out of plywood strung on fine twine and he had whirled them round and played with them.

"Don't want new friends," Shmuel said. Dora sighed

but she persisted. Shmuel looked at pictures with bright colours, flowers and butterflies.

"Are we going to the temple?" he asked, mollified.

"No, darling, we are going to meet children like yourself."

"Don't like children."

"You will like these children," Dora said. And now it became easier to tell the truth. "You will stay with them all day and sleep there too, but Mummy will visit you. You will have nice new clothes too, not embroidered robes but proper clothes like proper children wear. So let's roll these drawings up and take them back to the children. Their teacher is called Miss Letitia. You will like her too."

"Holy One carry the paintings," Shmuel said. Dora didn't attempt to correct this reversion to his former self.

And so Shmuel came to the home where the children worked their own healing in his damaged life.

It began with Srulek.

"See, my name's Shmuel too," the eleven year old boy said, seeing Shmuel crying in a corner of the play room.

"Soldiers don't cry," he added.

"Soldiers kill," Shmuel said, remembering things the Children of the Rising Sun had told him.

"Soldiers ride horseback without saddles and stirrups. They hold the reins with one hand, while with the other they hold their gun. They fight so that people won't have to die. I was a soldier. I rode in the forests."

"Did you have a gun?"

"Of course I had a gun. We all had guns. And I had a knife and a flag—a red flag. When our unit liberated the villages and towns the soldiers let me ride in first waving the flag. I liked that!"

Shmuel listened entranced. "What are saddles and stirrups and what was that you said?"

"What did I say?"

"Reins. Rain falls from the sky and then there are no butterflies. How can you hold rain?"

So Srulek explained how you could hold reins and Shmuel forgot to cry.

"Come, I'll draw you a picture of a horse and then you can see what a saddle is and stirrups and reins."

Shmuel felt a little shiver of pleasure run across his scalp and down his spine. He hadn't felt like this since the ministrations of the Children of the Rising Sun—and this was even better: Srulek was a boy like him. When Letitia looked in half an hour later Shmuel was sitting on the floor beside the older boy.

She smiled and closed the door. Troubles would come, she was sure, when Srulek and the older ones had to go to day school. But that would be for tomorrow. This evening the little boy was at peace. And she knew Srulek's sad heart. She remembered the way he screamed in his sleep. "Mummy, no, I won't do it, no! No!"

"Avenge your mother! Avenge, avenge!"

He'd looked around him, trapped. They'd been his comrades, these lads in their army uniforms. They'd taught him to ride and use a weapon. They'd taught him how to make a fire in the forest clearing. He'd learnt their language and sung their songs. Kalinka, Kalinka, Kalinka moya... He would ride with them all the way to Berlin and would see how they plundered houses with goods the like of which they had never seen. They would pull electric wiring from its sockets just to see how it worked. They'd never ridden a bike, these village boys from collective farms, and they stole children's ones, thinking that, lower to the ground, they would be easier to ride and less harm would be done in a fall. Srulek would see what they did to women too and he would understand what his own sister had been through—she was in the home with him, a mere two years older but a world apart in experience.

Yet she hadn't had to do what he had done...

They'd brought the prisoners from the defeated army into the forest clearing: beaten men, bedraggled, starving and full of fear. They'd abused them with all the filth they could heap upon them; and Srulek had recalled men in uniforms like these who had rounded up his people like dogs, how they'd loaded them all on to lorries—and how his mother had pushed himself and his sister to the back of the scrum—and had flung herself on the soldiers with their guns.

She hadn't spared herself. She'd died for him. Was he a coward that he couldn't curse these abject men from the enemy race? He'd seen soldiers like these strung on trees and he had told himself this was all part of war.

But—put out their eyes? No! No! The irons were heating.

"Come on you, brat, what are you waiting for? Avenge your mother, you lily-livered, degenerate trash."

His hand trembled as he took the red hot iron from the fire, he had hesitated, drawn back, but one of the comrades had gripped him hard and guided his hand with the smoking weapon towards the cringing victim's terror-struck face.

"No!"

Was it the soldier's screams or his own? He'd broken away and spewed up, retching until he had nothing left. He would never forget what he'd been made to do.

* * *

Srulek came up to Shmuel next morning.

"We talked about the forest last night," he reminded the little boy. "I miss the forest, the smell of meat cooking on an open fire, the rustle of the wind and the smell of the trees, kind of resiny and the different green shades of the leaves. I miss the quiet places and I miss the songs and the way we knew we were doing a great thing: setting people free. The Children of the Rising Sun are right when they want peace, not war, but if our soldiers hadn't fought, the war would still be going on and we would all be dead."

Shmuel blinked. He didn't like that sort of talk.

"Tell me how you rode your horse when the sun was rising among the trees."

But Srulek had to go to school.

Shmuel's lip went down. "I want to go with you. Take

me too."

"I can't. You're too little. You must stay with the younger ones.

"Don't want to. Want to come with you," Shmuel whined.

"Good soldiers do what they're told," Srulek said. He turned away to pick up his school bag. "I'll see you after school and you can tell me what you've done today."

Shmuel's mouth quivered. He managed to suppress his sobs until Srulek had left the room and then he flung himself on to the bed and howled.

Letitia found him.

"Come, Shmuel. You can draw butterflies and flowers and show them to Srulek when he comes home."

"Don't want to."

Letitia walked away. Lisa was off school today, seven year old Lisa who hadn't been able to stand up straight when she'd been found.

"Lisa, darling, there's a little boy called Shmuel who only knows about paper flowers and plywood butterflies," Letitia said. "I have to look after the little ones, but do you think…"

"Yes of course, Miss Letitia," Lisa smiled. "We'll go into the yard and pick flowers. I'll show him my flowerbed."

"That's just what I hoped you'd say. Thank you so much Lisa."

So Lisa went up to the huddled, sobbing boy—who was getting tired of his own rage.

"Hello. I'm Lisa. You must be, Shmuel."

"Want to go to school with Srulek," Shmuel sobbed, but he was interested enough to give a quick glance at the newcomer with her pale face and bouncy curls.

"Want to go to the forests. I never saw the sunshine."

"Nor did I," Lisa told him.

He looked round then, his tears dry. "Were you in a temple too?"

"Temple? What temple? No, I wasn't in a temple. I

didn't make plywood butterflies or paper flowers. I never saw a single butterfly. But now I've got a garden full of marigolds. I'm trying to grow chrysanthemums."

"Krysy -mums, that's funny!"

Lisa laughed too and Shmuel felt the same tingle of pleasure that he had felt when Srulek had offered to draw a horse for him.

"Chrysanthemums are flowers. It's a very hard word to spell."

"I want my mummy," Shmuel started to cry.

"I want my mummy too."

"Well, go and look for her then," Shmuel sniffed.

"I can't. She's dead. All my family are dead. I've got no one left. You're the luckiest boy in the world if you've got a mother. If you ever feel mad at something your Mum has said you should think of all the children who haven't got a mother."

"Like you." And now he felt a new sensation, something akin to pity for this little girl, as well as sadness that he had forced out of her the confession of her loss.

"Like me," Lisa agreed. "Come, Shmuel, put your jacket and outdoor shoes on. I want to show you my garden. Miss Letitia said that you can help me dig and plant new seeds and pull up weeds."

"What are weeds?" He let her lead him downstairs and out into the yard. Miss Letitia watched them through the nursery window.

* * *

When the elderly country-man, not quite right in the head as people said, had lifted her out of his wheelbarrow in the cemetery beyond the village, Lisa had felt quite happy at seeing trees and flowers, sunshine and shadows. She was five years old and had spent six months in the village; the last four weeks she'd been hiding in old Franek's one room home, cowering behind the stove whenever anyone came, or simply sitting on the floor, peeling potatoes for the thin soup Franek made ready, like a hare or deer, to dart away if danger drew

41

near.

And she was missing her Mummy and her brothers and sisters. The lack of them was a hollow ache which gnawed at her like hunger, but in a different way.

Mummy had taken her to the village. She had knocked at several cottages, a quiet tap at a door or window-pane. Sometimes dogs had chased them away. Lisa had wanted to scream but Mummy had held her hand all the more tightly and said, "Don't be afraid, don't make a noise." But Lisa was afraid. Most people had not responded to the gentle rap, some had opened up but closed the door as soon as they'd seen the haggard faces of the woman and her child. Too dangerous!

Mrs Dudka had taken them in—and agreed to keep the child, for a certain sum. Mummy paid and promised she would come again with more money. Lisa had tried not to cry as the door had closed and she was left alone with an ugly old woman with a headscarf knotted round her wobbly chin. Mummy was beautiful and kind and good.

Mummy had never come back again.

Mrs Dudka kept Lisa indoors all winter long. She made her sit still for hours on end, holding hanks of wool until her arms ached, while the old woman wound the wool and scolded the little girl if she let her arms go slack.

The wool itched and scratched across the child's unwashed skin.

Lisa had to learn to peel potatoes and scrub the floor and scour the battered pots and pans. Her dresses got too tight for her. She had to discard her shoes.

"Won't matter." Mrs Dudka said. "In winter you're never out and come summer you'll run barefoot with the other village brats."

Sometimes she beat Lisa, because she believed that was how to bring a child up.

"Had sixteen of my own," she said. Some had married and gone away, some had died, some had gone off to the army and not come back, some had…

Wherever they were, there were too many of them and when they arrived Lisa had to go into hiding, squashed for hours behind a sofa with an old boot for when she needed to pee—quieter than a pot, Mrs Dudka said.

Lisa began to forget her former life. Perhaps things would be better when the summer came though she dreaded the thought of village children. She did not imagine that they would be kind to her. Her one dream was that there would be a knock at the door and Mummy would come in and take her away from horrible Mrs Dudka and her horrible hut and everything would be all right again...

But instead of Mummy, enemy soldiers came to the next village and commandeered fodder for their horses and provisions for their men. Mrs Dudka took fright.

"Out you go, can't shelter you any more, it's too dangerous. Besides, your mother's never brought no more payment."

"But I have to stay here until Mummy collects me." Lisa's voice trembled.

"Well she hasn't come, has she, so just you get right away from here."

"I've got no coat, my shoes and dresses are too small."

"I can't help that. Your mum never gave me no money. Here, take this, I knitted it myself... It'll be a bit big, but it'll give you a covering. Never say I sent you away with nothing."

Mrs Dudka dragged some sort of sweater from the drawer and tossed it to Lisa who huddled into it. It trailed on the ground and the sleeves were too long. She might have giggled once at how funny they looked dangling down, but she had forgotten how to laugh. The wool was scratchy and the sweater smelt—she hated Mrs Dudka's smells...

"Out you go," Mrs Dudka opened the door.

Where to? Where to? Lisa remembered the barking dogs and the way Mummy had told her to be quiet and not to be afraid. Instinct told her to keep out of sight. She cowered in nooks and crannies along the village, diving for shelter behind haystacks or bushes if a person went past.

And that was how old Franek found her. She'd shrunk back, trembling, but he said, just as Mummy had done,

"Don't be afraid. Don't make a noise." And he had put out his big rough hand and helped her to her feet. "Thee mus' jus' come alonger oul Frankie," he said, his strange dialect whistling through his sparse yellow teeth. He spat out tobacco leaf and bundled her into a wheelbarrow and flung an empty sack on top. "Oh er, taters doin' fine," she heard him say as she was bounced and trundled along the unpaved road.

So Franek took her in and never beat her. He shared meals with her, often giving her the better bits. He hit the bottle sometimes and then he lay like a corpse while she wandered around his hut and wished he would wake up and stoke the stove because it had gone out and she was cold.

She was as unwashed as him, though her smells were different.

One day he said, "Oh er, them sodjers never let up and thou and oul Frankie we're jes going fer a liddle walk."

"Where to?"

"Thoul't see."

"Are you sending me away?"

"No, no, never fret. But t'ings is 'otting up. We mus' make shift and fin' a safer hiding place. See here, oul Frankie don' know too much but he knows one thing—we gotter keep thee hidden right out of sight. We've gotter keep thee safe, like. Frankie's found the very best place," he went on and once more she was bundled into the wheelbarrow, beside an old spade, covered with smelly, prickly sacking and trundled down the road.

"See now," he said, lifting her out.

Lisa stared at the trees above her. A few bright blue flowers grew in the long grass. She wanted to pick them, but Franek said, "None o' that, liddle 'un. Thee's gotter get outter sight."

"But where?" asked Lisa and she began to feel afraid. "There are no houses here."

"Now then, there's housen for them as u'll never give thee away," said Franek, mysteriously. "This be the graveyard, like and there's none so silent as the dead. See it belonged to you Hebrew folk, but there baint none left. Nobody never comes here. In you go." He hefted aside a stone slab. "It's a grand liddle hollow, jus' right for theesel."

"For me! You mean, I've to go into that hole? Oh, Frankie, please no, please, please," Lisa begged.

Franek took off his cap and scratched his head.

"What's to do?" he asked, puzzlement in his blue eyes. "Frankie'll not leave thee lonely here. Us'll come by each evening like with a bite for thee, mayhap thou'll run a little bit atween the graves to stretch thy legs by the light o the stars. There baint nothink else, liddle Lisa. In thou mus go."

She screamed when he shifted the heavy stone on top of her.

"Oh, never cry," his voice came muffled down to her. "Thou'll bring them here as we don' want to come. Frankie'll be back, never fear."

She kept quiet then, shivering in the damp, cold earth. She could sit up or lie, but not stand. She pulled up her knees and stared trembling into the dark. Later she heard voices: country children pastured their cows in the long grass which had begun to grow over the unvisited graves. True to his word, Franek came at night. He brought her food and covers. It was cold and the stars spangled the sky. Lisa tried to climb out but her legs were cramped and sore.

That night she heard the wind rattle through the branches of the trees above her hiding place. The rustle of the leaves sounded like voices whispering, uncanny voices like evil spirits come to snatch her away. She wet herself with fear and misery.

So day and night dragged away, seasons changed, but Lisa's cramped, dark world never changed. Hunger added to her other needs, for times were hard and Franek had been forced to beg. But whatever scraps of food he got, he scrupulously shared with his 'liddle Lisa'. She looked forward to his nocturnal visits, the sound of his footsteps, his whistling breath—he was her lifeline, her only contact with the living world. Some nights he didn't come and hunger tormented her, and then he'd re-appear, sobered and repentant. One day he told her that the war was coming to an end. The Red Army had crossed the frontier. The partisans had come out of the woods and the bad soldiers were being driven back. She understood little, but later she heard gunfire, shouts and screams. She trembled, thinking that the bad soldiers had come back to kill her and when the stone above her head was pulled back she shrank deeper into the dark earth. The rush of sunlight dazzled her. She hid her eyes. But the new soldiers wore different uniforms. And here was Franek's wrinkled, drink-flushed face.

"It's over now, liddle Lisa," he burbled, his voice thick with tears and vodka. Dazed, she tried to stand. With rough compassion the soldiers crowded round to look. One lifted her. She was too weak to struggle free. They took her to a woman in white with an odd looking tall white hat on her head. "Medsestra, nurse," the soldiers said.

Lisa was carried on a creaking cart in the rearguard of the victorious army into the burnt-out capital city and into Miss Letitia's care.

She never saw Franek again. Word got round that he'd sheltered a brat from *that lot* and some villagers, angry at the new regime, set fire to the old man's one room hut. Mercifully, vodka had blotted Franek out and he was unconscious when his few sticks of furniture went up in smoke—and his life ended in the blaze.

* * *

After school, Srulek found Lisa and Shmuel digging in Lisa's flowerbed and Shmuel showed the older boy an insect on his grubby palm.

"Look, Srulek, Lisa says it's a ladybird, God's little cow. Ladybird, ladybird, fly away home," he chanted.

"Lisa told me that song."

"And he knows it all already," Lisa's voice was warm

with praise. So Shmuel went on.

"Your house is on fire, your children have gone. But we're not burnt up. We're here."

"Yes, we're here," Lisa agreed.

"Let's set the ladybird free," Srulek suggested.

They watched the ladybird settle on newly-dug soil. Then they put their spades away and went in for bread and milk. So the young executioner and the entombed girl gave the little boy-god his lost childhood, and the mother who had found her son a second time opened her home and her heart to all three of them... Miss Letitia opened the orphanage journal and turned another page.

The River

Jan Kowalski's mother, a woman with greying hair, sparse teeth and a brood of children, shook her oldest son awake.

"Get off your backside, you loafing lout! They're emptying the ghetto. They say the Jews leave stacks of cash: gold sewn into mattresses, diamonds hidden under floorboards or in the heel of someone's forgotten shoe. Go on, you no-good bit of rubbish, just get along there quick."

Inside the ghetto that same war-torn day in early spring, amidst whistles, whips and machine gun fire, Dora Rottblatt, Leon's mother, choking back her tears, put a rucksack with half a loaf of bread and a change of clothing on her eleven year old son's back. "Run! It's your only chance. Go, my son, my lovely one. Perhaps we'll meet again when this madness is over." She pushed him away. "Go! Antlojft, bleibt leben Run away, quick—and live!"

Leon ran outside. Shots and screams rang in his ears. Shuddering with sobs he slithered over frozen pavements and stumbled through a gap in the fence that sealed off the ghetto in this small town.

Safely through the fence, Leon recognised streets where he had walked to school and played with friends before the world went mad. This had been his home once, but now he was alone. Death lurked at every corner.

Instinct took him away from the railway lines and those waiting trains. He ran towards the river. Spring sunshine had freed the water. It flowed fast, carrying broken pieces of ice, but the edges were still white with frost. Leon slipped and nearly fell. It was hard to tell whether he was walking on the bank or on snow-covered ice.

Jan Kowalski fastened his sheepskin coat, pulled on a woollen hat, stuffed a cloth bag into one of his pockets and stashed a bottle of home-brewed vodka away in an inside pocket. A swig would warm him and keep his spirits up.

Jan was no philosopher. He'd only completed three classes of primary school but the thing he was about to do screwed him up with distaste. The bloody Nazis have turned us into grave robbers, he thought bitterly, as he caught up with other people making their way towards the ghetto, eerily silent now. He avoided eye contact with these other tomb raiders: street-wise young guys who, like himself, had managed to dodge Hitler's labour gangs, or ragged, pinched urchins, some bowed women in shawls and a few older men.

They've made us slaves... we're on the edge of starvation.

Hey, what's that in the river? Must be something someone's chucked in. No, it's a dog. Poor beast is having a struggle.

Faintly from the frozen river came a thin cry for help.

My God, that sounds like a kid! *Do something someone!*

Jan turned towards people waiting at a tram stop.

"Hey, help! There's a child in the river."

People shuffled their feet on the frozen snow. Some turned and looked in the direction where Jan was pointing— and looked away as a tram rattled up. Everyone pushed on board. Jan was left alone.

Furious, he raced to the bank. The boy was still struggling in the icy water.

Passers-by noticed and stopped—two women and a man. The women were shouting, "Hang on, sonny! Hold on!"

A lot of use that was! There was only one thing to do, and Jan did it. He stepped gingerly on to the ice, lay down flat and edged forward. It was still okay here, the ice was thick enough, but the closer he got to the boy, the thinner it became. Splinters shivered across the ice underneath him. He wondered how deep the river was here. In the summer you could wade out almost as far as this, but it was swollen now and fast flowing.

"I can't hold on any more," the boy sobbed.

In fact, he wasn't holding on at all. His rucksack was holding him. The straps were caught to the drifting ice. If he pulled away, he would drown, but attached like that there was no way he could get himself back to the bank.

Jan stretched out over the cracking ice, grabbed the boy and pulled hard. Water swept up under him. His thick sheepskin kept most of it out. He wormed backwards, dragging the boy with him. He weighed next to nothing, even with waterlogged clothing. Jan helped him climb up the bank.

"The ice b-broke," the boy tried to explain with chattering teeth, but he could hardly speak for cold and fear.

"Don't worry, sonny. You're safe now," Jan tried to reassure him, but his heart was sick. Anyone could turn this small runaway over to the police—and his rescuer with him. Three witnesses were edging closer to eye the sodden survivor.

An abyss yawned, more dangerous than broken ice.

"Hey, folks, look what I've pulled out of the river! A Jew-boy from the ghetto! What shall we do with him? Chuck him back?"

Leon looked up with eyes full of fear. Jan squeezed his arm.

"What do you think, people?" he demanded. "Looks like he was meant to be rescued, eh?"

"The Gestapo won't think so," a woman muttered. "You'll swing for this."

Jan stared at her. Fear gripped him, as cold as the icy river. He fumbled inside his jacket. His hands were numb but he managed to pull out the bottle he'd tucked away.

"Have a drink on me. Best home-brew. Don't say where you got the booze from. Don't say anything about the kid either. You can tell the world about a guy that pulled a stray dog out of the river. Not a boy. Never tell anyone about the boy. Just keep your mouths shut, see. If you blab, well, I know people in this town, the kind of tough guys you don't want to have visiting your home at night. Silence is golden. Is it a deal?"

"Okay, just as you say," they muttered and drifted off along the bank. Jan waited till they were out of sight. He drew a deep breath.

"Well, kid, looks like we're in this together. Come on, strip off. Stick your wet things in here…" he held out the cloth bag. "That's it, down to the buff. You've got nothing to hide from Uncle Jan." He swung Leon up in his arms, tucking his sheepskin coat around them both. "You're coming home with me, you poor little kid, so just take that frightened look out of your eyes. You're all right now. Uncle Jan will keep you safe."

"Whatever's this?" Mrs Kowalska stormed. "Worse than useless, that's what you are! I send you out to get loot and look what you come back with! You'll have us shot. They'll take us to the market square and hang the lot of us, the kids, me, you and that brat you've brought in from nowhere. He could be infectious. We'll catch typhus and die."

"Calm down, Mam. It's going to be all right. Leon will work for his keep," Jan told her. "He'll help me roll cigarettes. What else can you do, Leon?"

"My grandfather made fur hats," Leon stammered. "He let me help sometimes. And Mummy…" he faltered. "Mummy makes paper flowers. I watched her do it."

"So there you are," Jan said. "We'll roll cigarettes, you show us how to make hats and flowers and we'll survive."

"Survive! With a Jewish kid in the house?" Mrs Kowalska screamed. "Work? I've never seen you do a day's work in your life."

Jan didn't bother to argue. He pulled the sofa out from the wall.

"See there, if anyone comes Leon can hide behind there." He turned to his brothers and sisters and put his finger to his lips. "You lot won't tell, will you? Leon's our cousin, see," he added with a wink which made them laugh.

Just as Jan had said, Leon rolled hundreds and thousands of cigarettes. The Kowalski children sold them in the market square. Leon cut and sewed hats out of felt and fur

—Mrs Kowalska and her eldest girls scavenged for materials. He showed the younger children how to make paper flowers. The money they earned kept the Kowalski
family better fed than they had been even before the war.

"I've never seen you work the way you do now, Jan," Mrs Kowalska said one evening. "I tell you, it was a lucky day when you pulled Leon out of the river."

Leon looked up; his dark eyes smiled, but behind the smile, dulling it, lay the deep sorrow of loss. "Perhaps we'll meet again," his mother had said.

But Leon knew, although the truth was so monstrous his mind couldn't grasp it. The dark place in his heart, icy and black as the swirling river told him all he needed to know.

He never left the Kowalski's single room. Too dangerous, Jan said, and Leon stuck to that even when Jan left home to join the partisans. The Russian Front was coming closer. The first Red Army tanks rumbled through the streets, followed by foot soldiers and a detachment of "boys from the forest"—the partisans.

People waved and cheered when they saw their local heroes, but suddenly there was a round of machine gun fire, a last stand by the defeated retreating army. Everyone rushed for cover, but one of the partisans fell. Leon, watching from behind the curtains, was about to dive out of sight when he saw another man sprint out of hiding to drag his injured comrade to safety. Jan! *Jan, no!* his heart shouted. *Go back! It's too dangerous.* Almost as though he'd heard, Jan ducked into a doorway and Leon breathed freely. The shooting stopped. Leon went back to his work at the kitchen table. Mother Kowalska was stirring soup. No-one saw Jan edge carefully back towards his wounded comrade. They all heard the gun-fire, a final burst from retreating soldiers. Red stained the white as Jan Kowalski lay dying in the snow.

* * *

Sixty years later, the Kowalski family received a medal:

"For Valour. Whoever saves one life saves the world."
Leon travelled from Israel for the ceremony. Amidst tears and
laughter he hugged Jan's white-haired brothers and sisters.

"I'll never forget being in that river. I knew I was going
to die—and then I saw Jan crawling across the ice."

Yet Jan would have said he was just a loafing lout on
his way to plunder the homes of murdered people that early
spring when a small boy had been caught by the straps of his
rucksack to a piece of broken ice in the river.

In the burial ground beside the river Leon placed a
single rose on the grave where Jan's body lay.

The Birthday Present

One of the other women in our group had a story to tell. "We've heard Jenny's story about Freyde, Danuta's about her father's lost love, Joanna's story about the mezuzah case, and now, I want to tell you about my grandfather, Slawek.

"I didn't know my grandfather that well," Kate went on. "He lived in Manchester. I grew up in the country near Windsor, all green and lush, apart from the traffic. I didn't like Manchester and, to be honest, I didn't really like Grandfather. He smoked a lot and his moustache was a kind of brownish yellow. I didn't like his hands, either. They scared me, and he spoke in this funny Polish accent—well, Mum told me it was Polish. And yet you see, even though I didn't like him, his Polish connections have led me here to teach music in Warsaw."

We all smiled at that. Poland has a way of getting into you.

"Grandfather came from the Borderlands. It's not even Polish any more."

The Borderlands, Kate told us, are the least known and least visited corners of Europe. Summer fields shimmer with the gold of ripening wheat, the silver of rye, with snow-white buckwheat and the bright amber of mustard flowers which invade the corn. It is all exactly as the poem says, that poem by Poland's national poet, which begins, O, my native land, you are like health. Only those who have lost you know how much to appreciate you.

Along with so much else, Poland lost these Borderlands, but there are still families there who speak Polish, pray in Polish, visit relatives in Poland. These families awoke one morning when the war had ended to learn that they could apply to be 'resettled' in Poland.

"But this is Poland..."

Not any more, they were told. This is the Union of Soviet Socialist Republics. Poland begins further west now—and this is official, it has been approved by the Allies...

Kate explained that in 1947 her grandfather Slawek's brother Joseph decided to join this new 'resettlement' programme.

"Life will be better over there," he tried to reassure his parents. "I'll send you food and clothes."

"I've lost one son," his mother put the corner of her floral pinafore to her red-rimmed blue eyes

"Mother mine, maybe I'll find Slawek over there..."

"'Lawek," repeated five year old Elunia, the baby of the family, born two months after Slawek had...

Not come back home.

Been taken away...

Or...

Mother Marta sighed and went to help Joseph pack his bags. She saw his gaze wander around their kitchen. She too looked as though for the last time at the painted jug and platters on the shelf, the picture of Our Lady of the Dawn Gates above the door, and at the sepia photograph of Marta and Witold on their wedding day. Beside them were snapshots of Slawek and Joseph, solemn in starched shirts, holding candles for their first Holy Communion: three years between those two brothers, the one flaxen haired, the other dark... In front of those photographs lay a long black box.

Slawek's birthday present...

Unlucky thirteen.

Marta, Witold and Elunia went to the railway to wave Joseph goodbye. He joined scores of other "repatriates", all being transported westwards to "Poland's regained territories."

Like the other travellers Joseph carried in his bag a little tin of Borderlands earth, Polish until so recently, Soviet now, his native soil whatever name it went by.

Joseph never saw his parents again.

He sent the promised parcels though, and wrote letters home—after all, Poland was a comrade in the Warsaw Pact. Elunia, her childish letters full of spelling mistakes, replied. Her letters became less frequent as the years went by. Some went missing, but most arrived until one day, twenty long years since he had left his home, Joseph sent a letter, *Slawek is alive. He lives in England.* Four years later another letter said, *Slawek is coming to visit me. Let you, Elunia, get your papers in order. You must apply for permission to travel to Poland. There's a train through Grodno. You get to the border at Kuznica. They change the wheels there. The Polish railway tracks are a different size. Don't get off—they'll put your coach on to a Polish train.*

Elunia, by now a mother of three, packed a small bag to go and see the brother she had not met for twenty-five years and that other one, the one from England, the brother she had never seen. Widow Marta, wrinkled and toothless, her sparse hair white beneath her floral scarf, said, "Stretch up, Elunia, and reach down that black box on the shelf. You must take it to Slawek. Take his birthday present that's been waiting here for so long." Tears filled her faded eyes. "So long," she whispered, rocking to and fro on the painted stool beside the kitchen table.

Ever since…

Flaxen haired Slawek, growing up in the village spread like a half moon on the shore of the lake, fished and swam with Joseph and the other boys. He could handle an axe by the time he was ten. He brought home firewood from the forest. He could tell the difference between the tracks of badger and hare, of fox and weasel. He gathered mushrooms and berries and knew which were poisonous and which were safe to eat.

During the long winters the village children had lessons in the school house, carrying bundles of wood to school to heat the stove. In Slawek's first years at school he heard the story of Poland. He learnt about invading powers, battles and generals. At home he spoke the dialect of the Borderlands. In school he learnt correct Polish. He stood stiffly with the other children and said the Lord's Prayer and 'Hail, Mary...' He recited the national catechism too: Who are you?—a little Polish boy. What is your sign? The White Eagle. Where is your homeland? Poland. What will you do when you're grown? Fight for her freedom and defend the right.

Slawek wasn't a great one for reading but he liked it when the teacher read the Trilogy of Polish derring-do. But then the Second World War began and two terrorist powers carved up Poland between them. The Borderlands were now part of the Union of Soviet Socialist Republics, "liberated" by the Red Army and controlled by Stalin in Moscow. The new regime brought new heroes. The children learnt about them in Russian.

Above all, though, Slawek liked to sing. Although the authorities discouraged church services, the school music teacher managed to keep on working as parish organist. "You have an excellent ear and perfect pitch," he told Slawek.

Slawek had no idea what he meant, but the teacher visited his parents one evening in early spring when the boys were being drilled as young Soviet soldiers by a leader who wore a star in his cap and was loaded with badges and orders of merit.

"He has a voice like an angel," Pan Laski enthused. "Does he play any instruments?"

Witold and Marta looked astounded. Instruments? That was for the gentry who had lived in the Manor House before the Red Army drove them away...

"The gentleman knows that we are poor people," Witold began. Marta nodded, but maternal pride made her speak up. "If it please the gentleman, when our son pastures our cow he plays pipes he makes himself from reed and willow."

"What does he play?" Pan Laski asked.

"Pipes, please, sir," Marta replied, surprised.

"I mean, what tunes does he play?"

"He plays the songs we sing in winter by the stove, Christmas songs and Easter hymns, the songs my mother and granny and great granny sang, just simple things."

"Just simple things," the choirmaster nodded, "Ah, Slawek's mother, the soul of a people is in its songs. I have come this evening to ask if you will give your permission—remember what that means in the present time—for Slawek to sing solo in church on Easter Day"

Although Red Army security forces surrounded the village church, the Polish community still brought their eggs and Easter cake to be blessed. There was standing room only on Easter Day when Slawek sang a solo in the idiom of the Borderlands:

we glimpse Christ's footprints on the earth; he quickens us, brings new birth: alleluia...

There had been a flurry of thin snowflakes earlier that morning, but now the sun slanted through the windows and haloed Slawek's fair head as his voice rang round the whitewashed walls of the village church. Villagers lifted war-weary, weather-beaten faces to the light. Many—and not only the women—had tears in their eyes as they listened to the young boy's song.

But then, a surprise, as the villagers thronged the front of the church to receive the holy wafer, music rang out once more, not the organ they were used to, but a flute, vibrant and almost trumpet-like in intensity. The melody was simple—it had to be because the flautist was a beginner. He was hidden in the organ loft, but Marta knew that the unseen musician was her son.

"I lent him my flute. He has a natural touch, the way he puts his lips to the mouthpiece, it's like a trained musician," Pan Laski confided on a furtive visit to Slawek's home. "There's a great future ahead of him, if only..."

Under the new regime, the teacher continued, there were opportunities for talent: music school in Vilnius, further studies in Moscow even, or Leningrad. But he would have to become a young Pioneer first, and then a young Communist, a Komsomol …

"Never!" said Marta fervently.

But she knew in her heart of hearts that if she could get hold of a good instrument for him—if… then, God forgive her, why should her son not have a chance?

She didn't dare tell his father, nor confess these thoughts to the parish priest, but her heart was swollen with pride and truly natural longings for Slawek to develop his gift.

But how could she ever hope to get him a proper concert flute?

The tide of war turned. The Red Army fled before quick-stepping young soldiers who marched across peaceful meadows, along dusty roads and through the wooden villages and the crowded Jewish towns of the Borderlands.

These changes brought young Shlome, ages with Slawek, to the door as Marta was lighting the kerosene lamp.

"The Germans are putting us into a ghetto," Shlome said, his Borderlands speech singing with a melody of its own. "Grandfather asks kindly if my friend Slawek's good Mother would please buy our cow?"

Witold, stuffing tobacco into his pipe, grumbled, "We don't have enough fodder for our own kye…" But Marta put her hand under the boy's patched elbow and drew him out into the shadowy porch. "Yes, sonny, we'll buy the beast, and you'd better take some of my apple pie, it's just about to come out of the oven. But Shlome, tell me something…" her voice dropped to a whisper. "Your uncle, the one who played in the dance bands on the ship, will he be taking his flute into the ghetto?"

"My uncle…" Shlome began. His voice cracked. He choked out the words. "Does Goodwife Marta not know…?"

"No, no… what is it, Shlome? Those executions… The men they hanged… Pan Laski the church organist, poor man. They got him as well. But not your uncle too?"

Shlome nodded, struggled, said, "He could have stayed in America. He came home to Granny. They said he collaborated with the Communists."

"Like Pan Laski," Marta sighed. "That's how he kept the church music going."

"My uncle worked in the Town Hall…"

"Yes," she said, "come now and get the apple cake."

A week later, her basket full of baking, Marta made her way to Shlome's house. She returned with a birthday present hidden under a much-laundered tea towel.

"We'll give it to Slawek when he comes home from work," she told Witold, unpacking it when their son, (no longer allowed to attend school because the German occupiers wanted to turn Poles into a servant class) was at work in the fields with forced labour gangs.

With work-worn fingers she lifted the flute from its box. It was dark wood, "Mahogany," Witold guessed. "Although maybe no, it's a shade too red, some other foreign stuff."

The flute was in three sections. The head piece was stamped with a name, Rudall Carte, 1925. Neither Marta nor Witold could decipher the lettering.

"Slawek will know how to put it all together," she said.

But at work that day Slawek's fair hair and blue eyes caught the attention of a Nazi 'nurse' in a belted brown coat. He was taken away to be turned into a good German.

* * *

"You had it lucky, though, in the end," Joseph told his balding brother in that high rise bed-sit with its view over the lit windows of similar blocks. "You got freed by the Brits, but we've…"

"Got Communism" Elunia added. "Easier for you in Poland, Joey, dear, than for us in the east."

Slawek looked from one to the other. He'd unloaded his presents, they'd downed a few vodkas, eaten rye bread, herring, gherkins and garlic sausage, passed photographs around—his were coloured, the others were black and white.

They'd looked at smiling nieces and nephews, cousins who had never met and wouldn't be able to speak to each other if they did.

And all the time Slawek watched Elunia. "You remind me..." he began. His blue eyes reddened. He lit a cigarette with a fumbling hand. "Of Mam last time I saw her," he managed to get the words out.

"Mam? You think so? She never wore lipstick or coloured her hair. She gave me this, by the way." Elunia put a well-washed string bag on the table and pulled out dried mushrooms wrapped in The Peoples' Paper, to take to the family in Manchester, as well as two large glass jars of their own fruit preserves and a long black box.

"What's this?"

"I recognize that box. It's your birthday present," Joseph said in a rush. "Mother kept it on top of the stove. She never let us touch it."

"Nor any of my kids either," Elunia added. "'It's Slawek's'," she always said. 'I got it for his thirteenth birthday'."

"My thirteenth birthday? But I..." Slawek lit another cigarette.

"She bought it off Shlome's folks," Joseph recalled. "Remember they sold us their cow?"

"I remember," Slawek nodded. "Lucky, you said, Joey... They put me to a German boarding school. Prison, I would call it. I ran away, but they caught me. They pinned a letter 'p' on my clothes. 'Polish pig,' they said. They sent me to work in a saw mill. I was the youngest there. One of the prisoners gave me a pill everyday. I didn't want to take it but he told me it would keep me strong. So I took it and survived."

"It was some sort of vitamin pill," Kate told us. "That guy sacrificed his own health for my grandfather's."

"So, lucky, yes, to be alive. But then... the accident. They put me in hospital, if you can call it that. The surgeon was a butcher in a white coat. I managed to get away. I hid on a boat going to Denmark. I got there more dead than alive. A doctor found me, a real doctor this time. He patched me up. I got put in a camp for D.Ps – displaced persons. I wanted to go home but my mates told me the Reds would put us in prison. They made me drunk so I missed the convoy. That's how I got across to Manchester. I was still only a teenager. I tried to contact you. There were agencies that helped Poles find relatives in Poland, but you weren't in Poland any more. I never gave up, though."

"And now here we are after all these years." Elunia's red-lipped smile revealed metal teeth. "And here's your birthday present."

"You'd better open it for me."

Joseph took the box. The leather veneer was ragged. He opened the lid. The flute lay in three pieces on faded red velvet. Slawek laid his right hand over the dull metal keys. His left hand touched the head-piece: two scarred stumps on the right hand, one on the left....

"Let's empty that vodka," Joseph reached for Slawek's glass. "There's music in bottles and you don't need fingers to play."

A Grandmother's Secret

Old houses keep secrets. This quiet room, its net curtains hiding the birch trees opposite, breathes stories. The highly polished oak table, well over a hundred years old, is empty now, except for a crystal vase filled with flowers. There were always flowers because there were always guests. Birthdays and name-days, Christmas, Easter... all were celebrated with abundance and fun, in the traditional Polish way. The best bison grass vodka accompanied toasts and afterwards there would be good brandy, great coffee and Halina's home-made apple sponge cake topped hugely with cream.

Nothing was stinted, nothing spared—except beds. There was seldom a sleeping space to spare. Four growing young people, their friends, relatives, guests old and young—the house was always full, and Halina washed and cooked and welcomed us all, for I too was one of those who felt this house to be a home from home. The journey on a suburban train out of Warsaw, leaving grey streets and state shops, a gloomy shared hostel room, was followed by the pleasure of the short walk from the station with only an occasional farm-cart or an old-fashioned bicycle bumping by. Once a nun trundled past, her cheery red face glowing beneath her wimple. She was perched on the back of a cart pulled by a poor and patient horse. The driver, stolid and silent, was muffled in ragged sheepskins against the cold.

I loved this walk away from the city—especially because I knew that the warmest of warm welcomes awaited me. An open door, smiles, kisses on hand and cheeks, sheepskin slippers and the wonderful invitation, "We invite you to the table."

I learnt the art of eating well in socialist Poland—at this house and with this family when all else was bleak and bare. Other young people had thin pale faces with dark shadows under their eyes and complained of kidney or liver pains, but Halina's four young ones glowed with health, fed well by their mother and taken by their father to the Tatra mountains on his motor-bike, each one in turn riding in the side car.

The young ones have long since grown and the old ones have passed away, but their stories remain in this room that was the hub of the house. Here are the sports trophies both parents won before the Second World War. Mariusz was a champion speed skater and Halina an award-winning runner. Great silver cups, shields, medals: these well-polished prizes fill an entire glass cabinet. Two oil paintings, the work of Mariusz, a talented artist, show, on the one hand, a lake in Mazury, drowned in green, while on the opposite wall a large framed painting hauntingly tells the story of Poland: an empty road, bare earth—we may imagine the armies of many nations that marched across this low-lying landscape to conquer and invade.

"We study history to find out who invaded us and why," wrote one of the daughters of this family when she was nine.

Other pictures in the room also tell the Polish story. A framed certificate, source of pride to all the family, was awarded to their grandfather for his defence of Warsaw in 1920, and beside that is a pen and ink portrait of General Piłsudski who magnificently salutes the country he led back on to the map of Europe—that portrait and that name were both strictly forbidden in People's Poland.

For Mariusz and Halina defied the controlled economy of People's Poland and the secret behind the loaded table was their ingenuity and sheer hard work. The only shop in the suburban township was state run. Halina, who swore with wit and vigour at servile politicians who mismanaged the Polish state, rose before dawn and cycled out to private markets where farmers traded wholesome vegetables and meat never seen in Warsaw. Shop windows in the city displayed outsize portraits of the prime minister, while inside were a few scraggy cuts of meat for which women queued, but Halina's larder groaned with fruit and vegetables she herself had grown—and yet her work-reddened hands could sew a delicate seam and darn invisibly.

There were always toilet rolls in the bathroom—an almost unheard luxury, because Halina offered the use of her telephone (as well as tea and a chat) to the woman who ran a newsagent's kiosk near the house, and in return, her supply of coarse thick toilet paper seldom ran out. Also, as friends and family managed visits to the west, packets of washing powder, Persil "washes whiter" and Tide stood on the top of the cupboard, bold propaganda flags.

In her old age, her memory gone, Halina welcomed me like the young girl she had once known. We sat together in the garden, in the shade of the walnut trees. Her hands were at rest at last, but her mind was restless, she still wanted to be the hostess, wanted to put her guest at ease.

"How many children have you, madam? Oh, my dear, you are far too young!!

And then she leant forward, and asked, "What are your secrets, dear? Every woman should have secrets of her own."

She told me how, during the war, she had buried her wedding china, white porcelain, edged with silver and afterwards had dug it up, piece by piece and transported it carefully home on her bicycle, with great secrecy and bravery, for there were robbers and blackmailers at every corner of the ruined streets.

"Rogues, scoundrels, that's what came to the top in People's Poland, but you won't remember that, madam, you are far too young. Now, tell me," bending forward again, "What are your secrets, dear? Every woman should have her own secrets, you know."

She died in her ninetieth year. I visited her grave, well-tended by her daughter Ania, who had cared for both parents throughout their deep old age—but it was after that, back in Scotland, travelling on an intercity bus from Aberdeen that I discovered something that Halina had not told me as I had sat with her under the walnut trees.

The bus was busy and at Dundee where people queued to board, an elderly man sat beside me.

He seemed a little anxious and asked. "Can you tell me please the stop for the airport?"

Pan (Mr) Adam had been visiting his family. His daughter and her husband had come across to live in Scotland, and yes, it had been difficult, but the grand-daughters had settled into school; both parents worked long hours but did not regret the step they had taken.

Talk turned to his own life, he had been eight years old when the Red Army approached the River Vistula and the people of Warsaw fought to drive out the occupying forces and, they hoped, to establish a free city before the Soviets got in.

But no realistic Allied aid came to the city that had resisted Hitler's tyranny for five long years and the enemy retaliation was brutal and total.

"We sheltered in cellars from air raids," Pan Adam recalled.

Soldiers tossed grenades into the building. Adam and his mother had watched their home go up in flames. The soldiers drove them out past houses with streams of fire pouring out of every window. People had snatched up whatever they could carry. One man had tucked a large oil painting under his arm; a woman had brought her pet budgie in its cage. On the terrifying march through a sea of fire the eight year old boy had seen dead bodies lying naked or covered with strips of bloodied rags. Armed partisans fired at the soldiers who forced three women to step forward, strapped machine guns around their shoulders and, firing from the guns had sheltered behind this human shield.

Herded through a city in flames, they had a momentary respite: a bowl of soup, but then the men had been marched away to become slave labourers in Germany. The women and children were driven on through a cordon of soldiers all the way through the suburbs of Warsaw. Their destination was Pruszków, a regional centre from which people, young and old, sick, wounded and dying were transported to concentration camps in Germany.

"There was no escape. They shot you if you tried to run away," Adam went on. "But suddenly we noticed a woman standing right out on the main road even though a German soldier was close beside her. She waved to my mother. 'Come, madam, come, save your little boy. Come!'

"So we made a run for it and our kind rescuer led us through ditches, fences and gardens to her house which was already overcrowded with refugees. 'I'm sorry,' she said. 'I can't take you in—but wait here, and I'll see if my neighbours can help.'

"Mother and I waited in the garden. It was a warm sunny day. The flowers were blooming. There were bees and butterflies; walnuts and apples were ripening on the trees. It was unbelievable, like stepping out of a nightmare, as if we had crossed from hell into Paradise.

"Our dear friend came back with smiles and good news. Her neighbours had agreed to help us and so she led us across her garden, through the fence and along a path to their house. And so we were saved, and do you know, even though I was so young, I still remember the name of this lady who rescued us, dear kind Pani Halina!"

"Halina! Oh, but I must tell her daughter Ania about this!"

Phone lines buzzed—and a few weeks later a call came from Ania. "Pan Adam has just visited me with a huge bunch of roses. I showed him photographs of my mother and he remembered her exactly. Then we went out to the garden and once again, he remembered everything. 'Yes, yes,' he kept saying. 'Here it is—this is the path Pani Halina led us along, here's where we crossed through to the neighbours!' What a wonderful co-incidence, that you happened to meet Pan Adam on a Scottish bus!"

"Polish - Scottish connections," we agreed.

Memories of Halina filled my thoughts long after our call was ended.

"What are your secrets, dear?" she had asked me under the walnut trees, and she had told me about hiding her dinner service, but of those she saved from fire and ash she said never a word. That secret went with her to the grave.

For Your Freedom and Ours

A brown bear and the Polish army
I was free, now I'm caged, that is why I'm weeping,
(Little Birds in a Cage, Ignacy Krasicki, 1735 – 1801)

Zoo... Doesn't have a smooth as honey, easy on the tongue, user-friendly sound. Not for any wild thing, and certainly not for a seven foot tall, beer and shhh... vodka drinking, fag-smoking, fart-performing, joke-loving, travel-loving, freedom-loving bachelor bear like me.

They call me Voy-tek but, write it Wojtek, in the Polish way. I was born free. My mother, her milk, her large soft body and our den in the mountains were all I knew.

Until MAN invaded my bear cub world. Not one man, many. Men with sticks that spat fire and smoke. Dogs that bit and tore. Men and dogs killed my mother and left me alone, too feeble even to catch small creeping things inside the cave. I dragged myself to the edge of the den, lifted my nose—and sniffed so many new smells, but my nose dropped back on my paws. I lay very still, about to die.

That's when something on two legs came along, another human, a small one this time.

"A brown bear! Lucky find! He will make me rich. Come on, bear."

The new small human scooped me into its arms. I growled and showed my teeth and got my nose slapped, hard. I whimpered, shocked, but this young kidnapper tossed me into a smelly sack and carried me down the mountainside away from my den, away from the hunting grounds where a bear could roam freely, away from my own kind into the world that humans know.

Engines hummed and halted. New smells. Tobacco, sweat. Voices, talk, tugs at the sack. I stuck my nose out, sniffing everything, frightened and oh, so hungry. The little human opened the sack wider. "It's my bear cub. First I will pull his teeth and claws then he will dance to my flute. We

69

will make much money."

A man picked me up. I growled and bared my teeth but he spoke softly and stroked my fur. Soon the little human was smiling, shouting goodbye with a mouth stuffed with food. It now had money and a big army knife. I had been sold to the soldiers.

* * *

The soldier who had taken the bear on his knee murmured soft words of encouragement: those first sounds of Polish spoken by a man who had known starvation and loss in the far north of Russia; life gutted on the knife edge of death.

"Nie bój się, mały. Don't be afraid."

The soldiers crowded around, curious to see the small furry creature. They tried to feed him and opened a tin of meat, but the cub wanted his mother and her milk. These men clearly had no idea how to look after a baby bear, but hands that could have harmed a small animal comforted him and soon the cub was slurping away happily at a bottle filled with milk with a rag stuffed in its neck

Their driver urged the soldiers to get back inside the canvas covered truck. The driver, saving fuel, switched off the engine and coasted downhill, swinging crazily around hairpin bends. The men were tossed from side to side, clutching hold of one another and swearing mightily, but without the roar of the engine they could talk more easily— and one big question was what to do with this small wild animal that had already endeared itself to them.

* * *

In the end they decided to say nothing. They were in transit across Iran and Iraq. Time enough to seek official permission to keep a bear cub once they reached base in Palestine where they were to train with the British Eighth Army and eventually fight their way into Occupied Europe and free Poland from two monstrous tyrants.

None of the soldiers could imagine how that was to happen, though they had plenty of opinions. There were huge issues to discuss—and if the little bear was one problem, there was another bigger issue in the shape of the Red Bear in Moscow. Stalin and his secret police had deported these Polish men and their families to slave labour camps beyond the Arctic Circle and the far reaches of the north. Frozen wastes beyond Archangel, the coal mines of Vorkuta, the gold mines of Kolyma, the cotton fields of Uzbekistan and Kazakhstan: the men and women who joined the Polish army under the command of General Władysław Anders had been forced to work beyond their strength on rations well below subsistence level. Many were blinded with lack of vitamins, sick with malaria, dysentery, typhus, malnourished and starving. Now they had to learn the technology of modern warfare—and look after a hungry orphan bear.

* * *

Well, that wasn't so hard for them, was it? They had plenty of empty vodka bottles for my milk—that's where I got the taste from, because, I'm telling you, I could knock it back with the best of them. So they had milk for me, while a tin bath and a few coarse army towels made a cosy cradle.

Soon they gave me into the care of a soldier called Piotr Prendyś but I needed my mum's big furry body. I clambered out of the bath and climbed into my soldier-mum's bed, and that's where I stayed for the rest of the night.

* * *

At their transit camps soldiers clustered round Piotr, a quiet dark haired man, already in his late forties, who won the men's respect by his gentle behaviour—and by being able to read and write letters for soldiers who had had no schooling.

"Hey, is this your bear cub, Prendyś? We heard you'd picked him up in the mountains. What's his name?"

"I decided to call him Wojtek lover of war—but he's a lover of fun, aren't you, little Wojtek?"

The cub pricked up his ears at the sound of his name and the soldiers laughed.

"He's a clever little cub—but will you be allowed to keep him? Won't they make you send him away to a zoo?" Piotr nodded. "That's what I'm afraid of." And soon enough, orders came for Piotr Prendyś and his baby bear to report to Major Chełmiński—who had already been apprised of the addition of a bear cub to the army and was prepared to regard the new arrival in a favourable light.

"So this is the bear cub? Well, Prendyś, I know soldiers often keep small animals as pets, but no way can we think of a bear as a small animal…"

Piotr made no reply and, as though he knew that his future was being decided, the cub sat very still.

"However, we are an unusual army."

Both men were silent, remembering how they had travelled thousands of miles through the vast Union of Soviet Socialist Republics to find the headquarters of the Polish army where General Anders had rescued Polish families from the gulags, whose horrors he heard of from the emaciated survivors.

I went out to the camp, small tents amongst the forests. The 6th infantry division was being formed there and for the first time I met the 17,000 strong contingent. I will never forget the way they looked. Most were without shoes or shirts. They were all in rags, some in scraps of old Polish uniforms, bony as skeletons covered with ulcers because of lack of vitamins, but they were all clean shaven. My heart missed a beat when I looked at these poor creatures and I asked myself inwardly whether it would be possible to create an army out of them and whether they would be able to endure the hardships of war that awaited them. But I knew the answer straight away. It was enough to look at their eyes shining with determination and faith. I went slowly through the ranks. The old solders wept like children during the Mass.... I stood to attention as they marched past and for the first and, God grant the last time

I took the salute from men without boots. And this parade showed that they were ready to march in step on those bare wounded feet on their long road home to Poland.

(Anders, *Bez ostatniego rodziału*, 1949, 2007, transl. Robertson)

Major Chełmiński pressed an official looking stamp on the page. "So that's that! Private Wojtek is now a Polish soldier."

"Thank you, sir!"

"Let's take a closer look at your cub. You know, in Lithuania where I'm from, landowners trained bears by making them walk over red hot floors."

Piotr shook his head. "That's shocking. I'm a farmer, sir. I respect animals. I hate it when they're treated badly."

"So what do you plan to do with your bear when the war is over, Prendyś? You won't want him in your farmyard, will you?"

Piotr smiled. "I come from the north-east of Volhynia, sir."

The Major nodded. "Plenty of wild places there for a bear to roam freely, forests and lakes and rivers where he can fish and swim. That's why we're fighting, isn't it? To get back the land we love, stolen from us. Our motto is *for your freedom and ours.*"

The Major patted the little cub. "Listen, Private Wojtek, soldiers obey orders—remember that, little bear."

But although Wojtek was now a soldier, he still crawled into Piotr's bed and snuggled up beside him at night and sought his comfort and reassurance when he bumped his nose or got frightened or upset.

* * *

Palestine... Iraq... In order to serve the British war effort in the Middle East the Transport Corps had to be motorised. Twenty thousand drivers were needed. Farmer Piotr Prendyś was well used to single horse-power: Piotr's chestnut mare had pulled his plough and wooden cart in summer and his sleigh in winter. When, on that darkest dawn in early February 1940, Red Army guards had forced the Prendyś family to leave their home, Piotr had cast a sad eye back to the stable where Star was munching hay and Krasula the family cow was moving about restlessly, needing to be milked.

"Don't look back at your horse and cow or pig," the guards jeered. "We have cows and pigs and horses in abundance. In the Soviet Union everything is for the people and the people have everything."

Piotr, who had fought the Bolsheviks in 1920, knew this was a lie, but horror of being transported into Soviet captivity along with his wife and children was too overwhelming for words.

Now, though, he had his brown bear—and Wojtek had his Polish farmer, plus the rest of the Polish army. There was always someone to play with and the little cub was everyone's favourite, full of fun and loving to tumble and fight with the soldiers.

Fights! The cub loved them! Up would go his paws and Piotr or another soldier would get ready to box. Cameras clicked. Men posed for their picture to be taken with the Polish Army's amazing bear. His photo was in the White Eagle, the Polish army newspaper and he even appeared on film.

* * *

I wandered through the camp on the lookout for some fun. The soldiers were on the parade ground so there was no one to play with—but wait! Little cloths hung on a long line. A breeze was blowing, and the things, whatever they were, moved with a flapping sound. I pulled one off the line, smelt it and realised that I could put these pieces of cloth on, just like I saw Piotr getting dressed every morning. I stuck my arm through one of the holes then wrapped another flowery thing around my neck. That was fun! I pulled down more and more pieces of cloth and put them all on me, as many as I could.

I heard screams, lots of running feet. I smelt people, but it was a different sort of smell from the soldiers I knew. Then I saw faces, but they weren't coming out to play, instead they were hiding inside their tents, peeking out to see what I would do next. Now that I had an audience I put on a show. A long stick supported the rope that the clothes hung from. I put it over one shoulder and marched up and down.

So there I was having fun, when Piotr ran up. I expected him to laugh and share the joke with me. I wanted to say,

Look, Piotr, I'm on parade!

But Piotr was angry and that always makes me sad. I sat down and let Piotr unwrap all those pieces of cloth from my fur.

"You should be ashamed of yourself. Those are ladies' undies!" Piotr's face went pink and those people with the human smell that wasn't quite like the soldiers' smell crowded around Piotr and me.

"I'm sorry, ladies, I'm so, so sorry," Piotr kept saying.

"Don't be scared of the bear. He's still only a baby, well, a toddler." And in answer to many questions he told our story.

"Poor little thing! But how brave you are, Lance-Corporal to tame a wild bear"

"Not at all. I'm so glad you put that call through to warn us that a wild bear was on the prowl. I knew at once who the bear was! Say sorry," Piotr ordered.

I hid my head in my paws.

"Ohhh!" sighed all the ladies. "What a pet. It's all right, darling, you didn't understand, did you? Here, have a sweet."

And now the ladies were pressing round me, laughing and talking, stroking my fur and giving me sweeties. So it was all right in the end.

* * *

Christmas Eve 1942. Wojtek was almost a year old and that evening when officers and soldiers sat side by side at tables covered with white cloths for the traditional Christmas Eve supper, the bear cub joined the party, seated on an upturned box. He soon got hold of a wine bottle and drank the lot. Piotr was horrified, but the bear was very happy. The soldiers started singing Christmas carols. Wojtek picked up a spoon and banged merrily on the table.

"Definitely not a party-pooper," the soldiers laughed, but talk turned to war.

"Stalin's Red Army will mop Hitler up. The Russian

winter will work against the Krauts."

"But the way to Berlin lies through Warsaw. Poland will be trapped between two opposing armies once again."

At this everybody leapt to their feet. "God protect Poland!" Wojtek got hold of the vodka, sniffed the bottle - and drank it all.

The strong alcohol rushed to his head. The floor rose up to meet him. He fell down flat.

The men burst out laughing.

"Ever heard of a bear with a sore head? You'll have to get him off to bed, Prendyś!"

"Too late. He's out for the count. Listen to him snoring."

When Wojtek woke up on Christmas morning he found himself alone in the canteen, extra ravenously hungry, but his nose led him to the right place as usual: the officer's kitchen where the hungry young bear soon created havoc. Pickled onions, cucumbers, beetroot, honey and jam: a flavoursome collage spread across the floor, to the horror of kitchen orderlies who came on duty.

"That bear must be punished," an officer said and Wojtek was tethered on a very short chain. He hung his head, whimpering sadly, but because it was Christmas he soon got a reprieve. Piotr unfastened the chain and the soldiers tossed the bear lit cigarettes, cheering when he swallowed them whole, and, a sure sign that he was forgiven, they let the bear have one small bottle of beer.

"He is not getting vodka," Piotr said firmly. "And all booze must be strictly rationed."

* * *

Booze, yes, well and good, but water… I could never get enough. The men had summer uniforms but the army hadn't issued me with a change of clothing. My fur coat was way too hot as summer temperatures soared. I was glad when we moved into the mountains where our camp had a shower hut. That was definitely the place for me! I soon worked out how to operate the showers—but when the men came back from manoeuvres there was no water left.

They kept the hut locked after that, but a bear never gives up; well, not this bear, and one early morning my patience was rewarded. I went off for a wander in the cool of the day, headed for the shower hut and, oh joy: it wasn't locked. I rushed in. A piercing scream hurt my ears and a man-smell hit my nose. I put out a paw to shake hands, but the intruder fell over with fright. Hearing his screams, sentries rushed in. The man fell to his knees.

"Help! Mercy! Save me!" he shouted.

The man was marched away. It turned out that he had been sent into the camp by local guerrilla fighters to steal weapons.

"Wojtek the Brave has saved the Polish Army!" Major Chełmiński declared. "You're allowed to stay under the showers until dinner time."

* * *

February 1944: the Polish Army was finally on its way to Italy but there was a bear shaped problem as the troops embarked at Alexandria. The British officer refused to let Wojtek go on board.

"What's this? A bear? On board a troop ship? Never heard such nonsense in all my life. There's nothing in the regulations about bears."

"Well, sir, if there's nothing in the regulations, it must be okay. Besides, the Polish boys have papers to prove that the bear is registered in their army."

"Papers? Let me see." Finally convinced that Wojtek the bear was indeed a Polish soldier, the British officer added his own stamp of approval and Private Wojtek went on board along with the other soldiers. Cameras clicked and troops of many nations hung over the rails laughing at Piotr and his bear.

"Hey, guys, the circus has come to town! Bring on the clowns."

They didn't need clowns with Wojtek around. The bear soon became the unofficial entertainer, a huge asset which helped the men forget for a few moments that warfare, wounding and death lay ahead.

Piotr kept the bear tied to the main mast. Wojtek climbed up and down this excellent five metre high climbing frame, to the accompaniment of cheers and applause.

Allied soldiers queued up to wrestle with the bear.

Wojtek always let two soldiers come up together and grabbed both men at once. One dodged away, but the bear trapped the other with one of his hind legs and the man collapsed on to the deck. Everyone laughed so Wojtek licked the soldier's face enthusiastically and rolled him back and forward. By now the man was certainly not amused. Wojtek let him get to his feet—then pulled his trousers down, turned the man upside down and stood him on his head!

"That's enough, Wojtek. Let Tommy go!"

Wojtek obeyed Piotr's command, and stood the man upright. The soldier pulled his trousers back up. His mates patted his back and sang "For he's a jolly good fe-e-e-ll-ow! And so say all of us!"

Wojtek beat his paw in time to the music—but soon the sea turned everyone upside down. Eventually, though, the storm blew away and the southern coast of Italy stretched ahead. The Allied leaders had decided to attack Rome from the south. Not only did formidable mountains lie in the way but the Germans had prepared a line of fortifications, the Gustav Line, stretching across Italy from east to west. Aware of the advancing Red Army, and knowing too how Stalin's noose was being pulled ever more tightly around Poland, General Anders had wanted the Allies to move up through the Balkans, but the order came that the Polish army was to join allied soldiers from many nations in attacking the now heavily bombed Monastery of Monte Cassino.

The Transport Company was to supply gun parts, ammunition and food to troops in the attacking line. The soldiers would be under gunfire from an enemy installed in secure mountain fortresses and to complicate matters, the whole mountainside had been heavily mined. The ensuing battle was primitive and bloody, involving cruel ascents, horrendous loss of life and hand to hand fighting—and it was in this appalling battle that Wojtek the bear distinguished himself and won his place in the history of modern warfare.

* * *

First the supplies got loaded on to trucks. But when the track up the mountain got too steep everything had to be off-loaded and carried on the backs of mules, until finally the soldiers had to transfer the loads to their own backs and carry them over the rocks.

They got shot at as they climbed so Piotr decided to leave me chained up at base. I heard his truck start up. I couldn't believe it! Piotr drove away without me. Piotr never ever left me behind.

I howled all night. No one could cheer me up.

That happened twice. On the third evening I got wise to what was going on and waited beside the passenger door. When Piotr arrived, carrying loads of equipment, I put my paw on his shoulder.

"You really want to come with us, don't you?" Piotr said.

In reply I murmured softly, and put my other fore paw on Piotr's other shoulder. We looked at one another. Piotr opened the door and I jumped into the cab.

Bears like to be out and about at night time—but not a night like this! We couldn't use headlights. At every bend we could have veered off the track to join the wreckage of other army trucks below.

The German air force attacked us from above. Bombs blasted the rocks around us. Splinters bounced against our windscreen.

Terrified, I tucked my head under Piotr's arm, but a bear like me always wants to be in the know, so I sat up straight again and sniffed the air.

During the day, when the guys were unloading heavy boxes filled with ammunition, I swung on trees that had been blasted to bits with war, explored caves in the mountains and then got bored. So that's when I made my amazing contribution to the war effort. I carried huge boxes of explosives, working hard along with all my soldier mates, carrying, they said, enough ammunition to blast Hitler off the face of the earth—to the horror of guys from the British Army who thought the mad Polacks and their crazy bear would send them all up sky high. But of course I didn't. I just worked alongside the soldiers. One of the men drew my picture: a brown bear with a live shell in his arms.

* * *

At nightfall, 11th May 1944 General Anders addressed his army,

"The hour of battle has come. The task that has fallen to us will bring world-wide glory to the name of the Polish soldier. The thoughts and the hearts of our whole nation are with us now. Go forward with faith in God and in our hearts our sacred watchword, *God, honour and the homeland.*"

The fighting was brutal. The Polish soldiers fought with reckless bravery that took heroism to new extremes. The mountain was torn apart by gunfire. The sight and sound and smell of death were everywhere. The fighting went on day and night until at first light on the 18th of May Polish soldiers entered the monastery ruins and raised a makeshift Polish flag. The battle had been won. No one cheered. They were exhausted and grieving for the many wounded. Then from the mountain heights a single bugle sounded a broken melody: the Polish hejnał, a sound as dear to Polish hearts the world over as the lone bagpiper on the battlements of Edinburgh Castle is for Scots.

After years of captivity, starvation and loss, now, in a place smelling of death, they heard in that melody a poignant sign of victory, of hope, of home. Skylarks sung and scarlet poppies, bright in the Italian sun, grew all over the blasted mountainside, strewn with broken weaponry and body parts. The poppies of Monte Cassino became a potent symbol for Poland.

The Italian campaign continued and Wojtek fought alongside the men but shocking news came from Poland. The Red Army had reached the River Vistula, but far from aiding the Warsaw Uprising, the so-called liberators waited on the banks while the Germans regained control of the city and started to burn it to the ground. Stalin installed a Communist-led government in Poland and having retaken Eastern Poland, he imposed new terrors on the country that the men of Anders army called their home.

The men felt sad and hopeless. Perhaps some of their black feeling got to their bear...

* * *

Perhaps it was just the way I always felt when I smelt a donkey. I went wild inside. My jaw shook. Long trails of saliva drooled out of my mouth and Piotr, who knew the signs, would always jump on my back, and put his hand over my eyes until I relaxed.

One terrible time, though, the wild feeling became too strong. A donkey was tied up in the field where we were parking our trucks. I raced across the field. The donkey broke free from its tether and ran for its life.

I chased after it.

Piotr cut across the field and stood between me and my prey. I reared up on my hind legs, roaring like the thunder of war and thrust my front paws forward. The claws stuck out like sharp knives.

"Stay, Wojtek. Sit! Sit!"

I came closer, ready to tear Piotr to bits. He didn't move.

What was I doing? Those wild feelings died away. I crawled towards Piotr and licked his feet, making little murmuring sounds deep in my throat.

Piotr stroked my head. I rolled over on my back. Piotr tickled my belly. I always loved that, but this time it meant that I was forgiven.

Piotr had saved our friendship for ever.

* * *

Wojtek the bear had become a war hero and the soldiers chose him as their company symbol. They wore their new Wojtek badge with pride. Then, finally the Second World War was over, but Poland had been turned into a police state ruled by Moscow. Warsaw was in ruins, and without anyone's consent, the allies had redrawn the map of Europe and Poland's borders had been pushed thousands of miles to the west. The beautiful countryside that the men knew as home had been incorporated into the Soviet Union. They could never go back. They would be shot or sent to a living death in the gulag—a hell that they had already endured.

Some officers committed suicide. Everyone felt the betrayal so deeply, and to rub salt into this incurable wound, not one Polish uniform was to be seen on the streets of London during the great victory parade. War heroes were executed and jailed in Poland; in the West their contribution was wiped out with silence.

The 22nd Company was broken up. Polish families were dispersed all over the world. A Polish Resettlement Corps was formed and Piotr signed up for Scotland, which meant that Wojtek was about to make another sea journey. Their destination was an old aerodrome in the Borders where Wojtek was allocated a hut of his own.

Wojtek was now fully grown, a massive seven feet in height with the muscular neck typical of his kind. His collar was now too tight for his powerful neck so Piotr made a metal hoop, lined with leather for greater comfort. He locked the hoop on the bear's leg so that a chain could be slotted into the hoop. Wojtek would not let any of the other ex-soldiers, not even those closest to him, fasten the chain, but so great was his trust that when Piotr came up with the chain the bear sat down at once and stuck his leg out to make it easier for him. He licked Piotr's face as he bent down towards him....

Piotr, who had lost so much, found his heart breaking within him. He was a fifty-one year old farmer without land living in a foreign country. He found a labouring job in

London in this country, impoverished by war, that no longer
wanted the Poles: and he worried about what was going to
happen to his trusting, lovable bear that had only known army

life, a war veteran now like the rest of the men?

"A zoo?"

"No way…!"

"Piotr, be reasonable! He would be well cared for."

"Wojtek in a cage? Never."

"Well, then, the kindest thing is to…"

No, it was unsayable, but one of the men said it
anyway. "The kindest thing would be to put him down. One
pistol shot. It's as simple as that. He would die like a soldier."

"Shoot Wojtek?"

That almost started a fight.

Archie Brown, who organised English classes for the
men, offered a suggestion.

"I met Wojtek when I was out in the Middle East.
Please believe me, your brown bear will stay in my heart for
ever. Suppose we lend Wojtek to Edinburgh Zoo, strictly on a
short term basis, for temporary safe keeping…."

Piotr knew the Scotsman meant well, but he just
couldn't agree. He rushed out into the damp night air and
pressed his head against the rough cast wall of the wash hut.
A dark figure loomed out of the night. His brown bear stood
beside him. Piotr buried his face in the bear's soft fur.

* * *

Oh, those autumn days when the wind roared through the
trees I had so much energy and an appetite to match. Having
carried ammunition it was no problem to me to heft huge logs
across the camp for the heating systems and cooking stoves. I
carried crates of food and rolled barrels of beer into the
cellars.

I needed a mate. I wanted to wander away, to go for
long walks. One evening a meeting was held inside the camp
so I went AWOL and headed across the countryside. A lorry
drove by. Well, I am a bear for the open road, so I moved

towards it. That freaked the driver out. He lost control, crashed the lorry and ran for his life.

Great! I love running races! The man shot up a tree. Better than ever. What a great game! I climbed up after him, ready to grab the fellow and bring him down to play with me.

His screams tore the evening air.

"Woj-tek! Woj-tek! Where are you? Come down from that tree and leave that poor guy alone!"

Oh, I was sad, but we know who is boss here, don't we? Very slowly I climbed back down, but then I smelt something that made me forget about climbing trees—beer.

"You have just been made a life-long member of the Scottish-Polish Friendship Society. We've brought you some beer in honour of the occasion."

Everyone clapped and I drank the beer happily. Then we went back to our huts. The guys sat around playing bridge. "Two no trumps…"

Young Stan laid down his cards—and oops! He went pink and everyone laughed. Then I let off too. I could trump with the best. My farts were famous. The men creased up with laughter. Helpless, we rolled around the floor—and the more I rolled the more the smells of my dinner, well flavoured with beer, wafted round the hut. The men rushed to open the windows and the door. They lit cigarettes and tossed me some too. As usual I swallowed the burning fags whole.

"Wojtek the champion! Wojtek the best!"

* * *

On 15 November 1947 an open lorry arrived at the camp. Wojtek jumped into the back; Piotr and his mate Jan climbed up beside him. The bear watched the countryside fly past until they arrived in town, turned off the main road and drove through a gateway. Wojtek's nose twitched. Perhaps he sensed strange animal smells. Men in uniform were waiting with chains in their hands and long metal rods. Jan looked away. Piotr swallowed hard.

"Come, Wojtek."

Man and bear walked into the cage together. Piotr knelt

down. He undid the metal hoop round the bear's leg and Wojtek stretched out his leg to help him, licked Piotr's face as usual then, curious as ever, started to explore the cage.

The men with rods shut the door.

The bear turned at the sound—and now for the first time he looked at Piotr through bars. The trusting look in the bear's brown eyes said, *I know you'll come back for me, Piotr, you always do.*

Wojtek heard Piotr walk away, heard a door shut, heard an engine start up—the sound that always brought him running to Piotr's side….

Wojtek would never run free again.

He spent the rest of his life in Edinburgh Zoo. His cage had a covered den at the back and an enclosure where the bear could wander. A deep ditch ran all round the enclosure, but it didn't stop his Polish friends from jumping across. These ex-army men delighted the crowd and horrified the keepers because, although it was strictly forbidden, they wrestled with the bear, just as they had always done.

Wojtek was still a crowd-puller, but he liked it best when he heard Polish spoken. He turned his head to those never-forgotten sounds; perhaps deep down he kept a glimmer of hope that Piotr would come back for him one day.

* * *

The old bear is lying in his warm den. His body twitches in his sleep. Memories float through his dreams like the butterflies he used to chase but never caught.

Farmer Piotr believed that animals can speak on Christmas Eve. Wojtek never spoke to the Polish soldiers, but it will soon be Christmas—it is snowing already. The snowflakes settle, but not like the deep snow Piotr remembered from Poland. The bear's ears twitch as the door into his den opens. Wojtek lifts his head. He hears the tap, tap of a stick—and a smell. The man smell that he loves so much and has missed so long. Piotr is an old man now. He lies down beside the bear and speaks very softly. His lips tickle the bear's ear.

"Well, old friend Wojtek, that plaque they put on your cage tells people who you are, but you and I know the whole story. We had good times together, didn't we?

"Remember how we found you in the mountains? Remember the fun we had, fighting and wrestling. You could have killed me a thousand times over, but you never did. Remember Monte Cassino? How you carried ammunition... That's how the world remembers you, Wojtek, but I remember my little bear cub, my big boxing bear, my faithful friend..."

Remember... remember... so many memories drifting by like butterflies.

Wojtek's big bear body relaxes. He no longer feels stiff and sore. He drifts into a sleep as sweet as honey, as warm as Piotr's love.

* * *

As warm as my love... but I never went back, although other Polish ex-combatants visited Edinburgh to see Wojtek and to have a drink in the restaurant where our great general, Stanisław Maczek, denied a war pension, worked behind the bar. But I had not enough money and how could I endure to see my bear behind bars, see him and part with him again?

No, I could never go back, but I never forgot. I did the one thing that in the end (though I didn't live to see it) kept Wojtek's name alive and ensured that neither he nor the Polish soldiers of Monte Cassino would be forgotten. I took the big stone that had been Wojtek's pillow to a meeting of Polish war veterans in London. There I became acquainted with an officer, Mr Lasocki, a writer. Mr Lasocki wrote the story of Wojtek in a book for Polish children in our great, scattered Polonia, so that the next generation of children, the generation of my grandchildren (for that blessing was granted to me in my exile) would learn about our crazy bear who drank too much beer and fought like a hero in Monte Cassino —to be rewarded, like ourselves with long captivity far from the beautiful home that we'd fought so hard to free.

* * *

On 2 December 1963 Wojtek died in Edinburgh Zoo. He was twenty-two years of age, his sight had gone, his joints were sore, his hearing diminished and he no longer willingly went out and about beyond his den. He died, his keeper Jack Foley said, a soldier's death, put down at last by a bullet, but his story lives on. Wojtek gave hope to soldiers in war time and became a warrior in his own right. This Syrian brown bear, born in Iran, who lived in Iraq, Palestine, Egypt and Italy and died in Scotland, has fans the world over. He has become a bear of peace, an emblem of unity between people everywhere.

The Terrible Trade of War
A German Grandfather Remembers

I am old now, very old. My grand-daughter, Helga's girl is in the USA, studying there. The Berlin Wall has already fallen, but in Israel they build another Wall. People speak about what Germans did to Jews. I was a soldier in Poland in 1944 and I saw only ethnic Germans—*Volksdeustsche*, Polish partisans, and Russians, but my grand-daughter, Helga's girl, tells me she has read that a young Jewish boy could perhaps survive the concentration camp if he says he knows a trade—if he walks tall through inspection and says, "I am eighteen. I am a cobbler, or a carpenter... I have already a trade."

I was eighteen in 1944 and I too had a trade: war. My trade was Hitler's war.

I finished school with good grades in 1942 and then worked with my father on our farm in Bauerhof in eastern Germany. However, I was ordered to do a junior officer's course in the Army. So great was the need for men in the Army that we completed that two year course in one year. We learned how to salute with the heels brought sharply together, how to greet and reply to our superiors, '*Jawohl, Herr Feldwebel!*' We learned kitchen work and cleaning work. There was much that was harsh and unpleasant but there was swimming, gymnastics and light athletics, good friends and laughter when the *Feldwebel* (sergeant) was not too near.

When I went on practical work, I saw beautiful Germany, Nuremberg, Heidelberg, the mountains—a great experience for a farm boy from Bauerhof. I did not know that I would never see that part of Germany again. It was peaceful and pleasant: walking in our uniforms through the streets of these nice old towns and enjoying the admiring looks of pretty girls. We did not want war, but we were at war and so we had to learn the trade of war.

We also saw the effects of war. We visited a hospital filled with severely wounded men, returnees from the Russian Front, many blind or without arms or legs.

"Keep smiling, boys," a comrade, Wilhelm told us. "It will hurt them more if they see how shocked we are."

We were very shocked, of course. At eighteen years of age, we could carry heavy weapons as we ran, we could prepare dug-outs in rocky as well as sandy soil, we could shoot at targets—but men without legs, men without arms, young men of our own age: these things we had not seen.

All around the hospital rose beautiful mountains. The sun shone on grassy slopes and bright wild flowers. If it had not been for those men and for our weapons and uniforms, war would have seemed very far away.

But it was our trade and we must learn it all. We were posted to Hitler's *General Gouvernement*, as Poland was called, to Toruń—we called it by the German name Thorn, as it had once been a historic Prussian fortress-town. Here we had to demonstrate all that we had learnt—to set up our positions and shoot at targets. Here we kept Christmas, my first Christmas away from home. Little did I know then how many, many more Christmasses I would spend in foreign parts—and far worse ones than the barracks in Thorn. I wonder now what I would have done if I had known what fate awaited me... but you cannot desert from the Army. You can only laugh with your mates and wink at pretty girls and down a schnapps or two in a bar, taking care not to be gated for coming back late.

They punished us for the slightest misdemeanour. Each day we had to march through the town to the shooting place. The marching parades were strictly supervised and we had to sing as we marched. And so we marched, singing Nazi songs and also folksongs that I liked better—*there is no lovelier land than the Fatherland...* I thought of the mountains we had seen in the south, I thought of the flat lands of my home, the red roofs of the houses, and the church tower set among such kindly trees. Perhaps my comrades thought of these things too as they marched and sang. Also, perhaps the townspeople of Thorn heard our songs, for although the streets were empty I saw curtains twitch in upstairs windows and knew, all unseen, people were listening to the song we sang. Our officers listened too—and if the singing didn't go so well, we had to practise all the songs again in our own free time. Needless to say, we always sang as heartily and loudly as we could.

I finished the course and was given two weeks' leave. I went home, met with mates of mine and we had good times. When I left home after that leave in April 1944, I was just nineteen. I didn't know I wouldn't see my home or family for twelve more years.

I did know that the good times had come to an end. For now we were posted to the Front, east of the town we called Lemberg. It had once been such a beautiful city. First it had belonged to Poland, then to the Austro-Hungarian Empire, then to Poland again but from 1945 it has belonged to Ukraine and is called Lvi'v. On the way there in the troop train we heard tragic news from home that the British and Americans were bombing our heavy industries, but I also heard that bombs had fallen near my home. The enemy planes had dropped their bombs right above Bauerhof. The little pub was hit where I had spent many happy times on my leave and the landlord who had filled my glass with extra beer had been killed.

From Lemberg, the Front was very close. My division was sent to join the Berlin-Brandenburg Division to guard the passes of the Carpathians. We were stationed in a town which is also now in Ukraine. On the very day of our arrival the Russians broke through with one hundred tanks. The narrow streets of the town were filled with Russian tanks, We were issued with anti-tank missiles and battle commenced. In two hours, peace was once again restored. Most of the tanks had been destroyed. A few managed to break away and escape, but most were shot to pieces in the streets of the town. Our special troops came to clean the debris away.

For the next months our division covered the whole of the country once known as Galicia. We dragged heavy weaponry through high mountain passes in the Carpathians and we traversed rolling meadows in the foothills of the East Beskidy mountains where old people still spoke soft southern German. Many of them, in whose homes we were quartered, still had portraits of the old Austrian Kaiser Franz Jozef. They welcomed us boys even though our armies had unrolled the whole theatre of war across their quiet lands where agriculture was still carried on in the most primitive ways. I think they were happier with us than with the armies that were approaching from the East.

Volunteers from the Asiatic lands of the Soviet Union carried our baggage and heavy weaponry. We called them Fiwis—*freiwilligen*. When the fighting got hot they simply disappeared. They were terrified of being caught by the Soviets because they would be the first to be put against a wall and shot. So we lugged our heavy weaponry over rough ground and with difficulty dug out the half moon trenches. Each one had to be 1.70 metres deep and big enough for the gun and for three men.

The tragic drama of war was played out in idyllic countryside of dreaming meadows, tranquil brooks and beautiful valleys. We would fight for a single position sixteen times, only for the Russians finally to break through and engulf the heights like a tidal wave. Once a friend from my training days, sub-lieutenant Wilhelm, the one who told us to keep smiling when we saw the maimed and injured men, came across to give us our briefing. All was quiet, a golden September evening with the remains of the summer sun sinking low over the hilltops, barely striking into the forests behind our camp.

"Well, boys, good to take a break," he joked, and we lit up, offering each other the tiny match flame, barely visible in the late evening sun. Suddenly from nowhere a grenade exploded, wiping Wilhelm out for ever. Splinters tore through the back of his head, smashing his skull to pieces. He stuttered something and fell into my arms. We tried to give him something to drink but he died, just like that. He was just one year older than me. There was nothing we could do. Next day we dug his grave. We laid our friend to rest in the shadow of the pines, made a cross from wood, hung his helmet on top and left him there for ever. But the scene stayed before my eyes for many months to come.

And now, such was the need for men to fight, I, with my nineteen summers, was put in charge of a batch of new recruits, every one of them old enough to be my father. I had to train these men in a crash course.

Our unit was ordered to free the stretch of railway line leading to Upper Silesia which had been captured by Polish partisans but the Red Army was coming ever closer. My unit with those old men, those raw recruits, was sent by railway right across Poland where we joined the 4th Tank Army. We were posted to the neighbourhood of Częstochowa. The shrine called the Black Madonna is in one of the many churches of the town. The population here is very devout and make many pilgrimages to this shrine. For strategic reasons, though, we were moved further west, so much closer now for me to my home. Polish peasants transported our heavy weapons and equipment as well as all our baggage.

Because of my rank I was quartered with a family that owned some land. They were Germans. Along with many of the villagers they had lived in Romania all their lives. Their forefathers had settled there in the sixteenth century forming a small German colony. They had emigrated to this part of Poland in 1940 when Hitler made it part of the Third Reich. There were about thirty villages there which were now occupied by these Germans from Romania. They had been given farms that once belonged to Polish families and there they carried on farming the land, but naturally, there was bad blood between these German farmers and the landless Poles.

I trained my recruits there, and there too, I kept Christmas with my landowning hosts. They had a daughter called Trudi and they wanted very much that I should fall in love with her, but Trudi was a plain girl with thin hair and thick glasses and although I was always very polite to her I did not want to kiss her. However, I was kind to her and went for walks with her, although I could have had my pick of many pretty girls as all the young men were away at war.

But, although we sang *Stille Nacht*, that Christmas Eve of 1944, there was the sound of fighting all about us. The Russians were breaking through and twelve days into 1945 came a major offensive. My old comrades from the division suffered major casualties and I never heard from them again. Whether they had fallen, went home free or were taken into Russian captivity, I don't know. Fate had decided that I should be spared, but we knew now that the peaceful time with our Romanian Germans was over. When we returned to the village, we found the houses deserted and every one of our kind hosts had fled. I never saw Trudi again, but I had no peace now to think of girls, even of those without glasses! We took provisions from the deserted homes—whatever the villagers had not managed to pack up and take with them. In early dawn we set off on foot, carrying all our heavy weapons. We stopped in a village and waited for two hours for the Field Commander to come with relief troops. He never came and we never learned the reason why. And so we tried to build a front. Winter came to the aid of the Red Army. The ice on the River Oder was so thick our machines could not break it up. So we had to hold the river, backed up against an old fortress. In spite of heavy fire we held out well at first, but then a single unit of the Red Army broke through, surrounded our posts and captured or killed them. Now the Russians had a trump card because the fortress had been used as a hospital for our wounded. Three of the nursing sisters, very devout Catholics, had decided to stay with the injured. The Russians used these elderly women as hostages.

The Russians laid waste to the whole place, pulled electric wiring from the walls, tore out light bulbs. And then they went wild. They gang raped and then killed those sisters. We retreated westwards. In the next village we saw a horrible sight. Sixty-five corpses decorated a defaced German memorial from the First World War. They were all civilians, Germans, aged fifteen or sixteen and old men in their seventies.

Later we learnt that Ukrainian girls who were forced labourers in the area had invited the Russians in and when they were well and truly drunk they had gone on the warpath and destroyed the village and massacred the people.

During that dreadful time I came across a deserted village. At first we thought all the inhabitants had fled, but then we saw women, old, young, even little girls hanging from the rafters of the houses. The Russians had not yet reached this place so we realised that the women had hanged themselves and their children rather than await their fate at the hands of the terrible hordes from the East.

We had to march on and hold out as well as we could. It was now February 1945. We held an old water mill with what weapons we had left. In that dark February night we witnessed an amazing spectacle. We heard rustling all around us, looked and saw about one hundred men without weapons slipping away across the ice of the River Oder. Then the Russians opened fire. Men were wiped out all around me, but Fate—or was it the good Lord—willed otherwise for me. We sheltered under the walls of a ruined house but soon I noticed that I was bleeding. I pulled off my coat and a huge splinter from a grenade fell out. My comrades bandaged my neck at once. We saw that the razor sharp splinter had pierced the collar of my greatcoat and cut through the material. So once again I had a lucky escape.

There was no way we could join forces with other units: we had no men and not enough weapons. On April 9th 1945 a comrade and I were sent to Kraków, the ancient capital of Poland, to fetch weapons for our unit. We were lucky. A few days later the Russians took Kraków, so we'd left just in time.

Spring came in with all its beauty. My mates and I went out to hunt birds. Beautiful woodland stretched out on all sides. It was simply lovely, a little spot of land that so many wars have been fought over; sometimes it had belonged to Poland, sometimes to Austria and now to Germany. But now for us it was the last stand of the war where we sustained our heaviest losses. It was so bitter—that so near the end of all that madness of war—that young men should lose their lives. Indeed we knew that the only thing that could save our poor remnant now would be a speedy end to war.

A small wood lay behind us. The Russians were ahead but we had no idea what dangers lay within the wood from Polish partisans and other guerrilla forces. Our whole unit had been pushed into this last tiny corner of Upper Silesia, once graced by a beautiful spa, right on the borders of old Bohemia.

Here on May 1st an important visitor arrived from our Army's High Command. With tears in his eyes, this man told us of the death of Adolf Hitler.

"In memory of our beloved Leader we will fight on to the very end," he said.

But we had to give up our positions. We fled across high mountains and in a lovely small town in what was then Czechoslovakia we gathered together in the market square. Here we learned on May 9th that the war had finally ended. We looked at one another. The end of misery and shame— and we had lived to see it! The way to freedom lay open before us. We were uncertain what to do.

"There will be trains," we were told, "going westwards, going home."

We boarded one of those trains, but before it had left the station it was surrounded by the Red Army. We were put on a train going east, not west. It was ten long, long years before I saw my family and home again.

So, one dictator, Hitler, took my youth and another, Stalin, the leader of the Union of Soviet Socialist Republics took my health. I have been caught between two tyrannies and when finally I returned, my native land, Eastern Germany, had been cut off from the West and had been put under Moscow's yoke. Freedom lay on the other side of a guarded wall. I have lived to see it fall. Will Helga's granddaughter in the USA ever read these words? Will her generation be wiser than mine? Or will they too be forced to learn the terrible trade of war?

This story is based on the memoir of Mr Herbert Sachse.
Grateful thanks to his family for permission to publish this version.

A Russian Grandfather Remembers

The little Lithuanian town of Provenishki is the place that has the most meaning for me on the entire planet. The tragedy that took place there, right before my eyes, still threatens my spiritual equilibrium every time I think about it, giving me a physical pain in my heart. Our unfortunate 854 regiment was literally wiped out by tanks.

Both battalions of the regiment had already been well and truly beaten-up. Not counting the remaining artillery and mortar divisions, there were just over two hundred men fit for action in the whole regiment.

That day, I remember, we went out to a forest clearing. A large field of rye and oats stretched out for about two kilometres in front of us. Small thatched cottages and barns were dotted around the field. At the far end the ground rose up slightly to the west and then plunged steeply down towards a river. The asphalt road leading to Kaunus stretched along the left of the field. As evening approached, Colonel Marfenkov, our regimental commander, summoned the commander of the first battalion and myself, a twenty year old captain, and ordered us to move forward, not in single file, but in formation like our Russian letter п, so that, as he said, it would be easier to manoeuvre.

To cross an open field in that formation was truly something new! It would only take one round of fire from an enemy artillery division and our regiment would no longer exist. So, once we had gone about a hundred metres in this novel arrangement, the battalions gradually stretched out into the normal chain formation and moved closer to the enemy.

We wondered what kind of enemy groups lay ahead, whether there was danger from tanks, who our neighbours were on the left or the right, or even if they were there at all —well, as usual it was beneath the dignity of our regimental commander to discuss all this with his subordinates. Apart from our basic rifles, sub-machine guns and hand machine guns we dragged one heavy machine gun along with us and two mortars. And that was our entire stock of weaponry. In other words we had no serious anti-tank kit at all.

We had just covered about a kilometre of the field when the Germans peppered us with machine gun fire and the battalions had to take cover. Dusk had already fallen and Marfenkov decided that we should spend the night there. For some strange reason the night passed peacefully. As a rule when the Germans were on the defensive they always kept up bursts of machine gun fire throughout the night but on that occasion there was no sound of gun fire all night long.

In the morning I noticed that my staff officer Sasha Solomatin was sitting gloomily beside me. Sasha, may his soul rest in peace—was unique in his own way. He could foresee people's future. He told me it was my fate to be wounded, but I'd make it through, live to have two sons and reach the age of eighty-five. And indeed, everything happened just as he said, except that last point which I'll check out five years from now.

That morning he told me of a terrible dream he'd had. A snake, a black adder, had bitten him. That meant that he'd die that day, of that he was sure. Sasha was an experienced, bold warrior, a survivor of gunfire and water, twice wounded, and decorated who never lost his presence of mind.

Everyone loved him, officers and men alike, for his humanity, kindness and humour. It's no exaggeration to say that he was the life and soul of the battalion. That's why I simply didn't recognise him—sullen, pale, his jaw trembling, his voice shaking. I'd never seen him wearing a helmet before, and here he was, putting one on, followed by two assault shields, one after the other. If a bullet or splinter got under their edge, they'd ricochet off both from the shield and the helmet. This way your chances of surviving increased. On the other hand, though, when you wore a helmet it was more difficult to hear the 'snoring sound' of the shell or the 'whine' of the mortar, besides, the shield was very uncomfortable, especially when you had to deal with a very personal, natural problem. I tried to calm him as best I could, but he clearly wasn't listening.

So the command came to move forward once more. A kilometre further on we took up our positions for launching offensive action. As before the Germans were silent, there was not a shot to be heard. My skin tingled as I sensed their presence, and the silence gave me no comfort. We were fully aware that there was no one either on our left or right flank. Stretching out behind us for two kilometres was that field, flat as a table; in front was the enemy whose strength and capabilities we could not know. One part of my battalion had taken cover in a small hollow at the base of which sedge and patches of hemp grew thick and tall. My staff and I along with the radio operators had spread out along the western slope of this hollow, in other words, closer to the enemy.

I summoned the company commanders and their seconds-in-command to make battle preparations. They sat down in a row in front of me. Two of them even took their boots off to freshen feet weary with much marching, but we had only just got down to the task when we heard the roar of tank engines. The senior telephone operator, who was about forty-five, old enough to be father to most of us and accordingly sometimes allowing himself a bit of familiarity, barked a command:

"Come on lads, get those boots back on quick, I have a hunch we've got to scarper." And at once we heard shouts from the look-out, "Tanks!"

Above the long grass I saw a whole avalanche of tanks coming right at us, ready to attack, I ordered the leaders of the squad to run for it with their men—and never saw the majority of them again either living or dead.

Unless he manages to dig himself up to his neck in the ground a soldier on foot confronted with a tank is doomed to perish. Well, we hadn't been sent out here to dig ourselves in, our orders were to attack. So the German tank drivers had one very simple task: to mow down the defenceless Russian infantry there on the open field. And that's what they did with all the professionalism, thoroughness and cruelty for which they are famous.

The fighting formation of the German tanks turned out to be wider than that of our battalions. Having come up on the slope and caught us in a semi-circle they fired on our disorganised, fleeing soldiers, killing a large number in one fell swoop. Then a total massacre began. The tanks chased the men, the gunners cut through their legs and the drivers mowed them down with the tank's caterpillar wheels. Practically the whole regiment was annihilated in just a few minutes, apart from a few men from my battalion who managed to hide in the hollow. The tanks didn't venture into the marsh for fear of getting stuck. The only thing left for us to do was to lie with our faces in the mud and hold our breath.

But that was unbearable for Sasha Solomatin who said to me in a voice which shook as he spoke,

"Captain, I can't stand this any more. I'm off."

I confess with all honesty that I felt utterly lost for the first time since the war began. I saw no way out of this horrible trap. It had all spiralled so quickly into a catastrophe that I couldn't decide what to do. I thought that Sasha had some sort of plan so I ordered him to take the political tutor and the radio operator and continue on as he thought best. I probably shouldn't have allowed him to go but it seems as though our fates had already been decided...

Because the last few men of my battalion were in that hollow I had to stay there too whether I wanted to or not. A few more minutes went by and I heard the rattle of caterpillar tracks from a tank which clearly belonged to the tank commander because the basic group of tanks had already got beyond the hollow and were finishing off the rest of our regiment further down the field. The tank went right up to the hollow, directly on top of me. I crawled just a bit to the left and the tank stopped so close that I could have touched its tracks with my hand. An attack by tanks is usually accompanied by the infantry which hunts the enemy out of every nook and cranny and covers territory that has already been captured, beating down any counter-attack. Tanks are vulnerable and not very effective in defensive action, so I pulled out my pistol, pushed the cartridge into the barrel and waited for the German infantry to appear. I decided that as soon as I caught sight of them I would pull myself up to my full height and start firing. That would be an easy death.

Suddenly "my" tank fired a shot into the field somewhere and then roared into action. It went into reverse and went back along the hollow towards which three more tanks were coming from different directions. They began to riddle the marsh with crossfire from guns and machine guns. I was lying on top of a grassy slope and that's what saved me. Anyone who hadn't been able to hold out any more and had started to run was killed either by machine gun fire or by shrapnel. I remember seeing Lieutenant Bragin start to run off. He was just a young lad in charge of a mortar-throwing unit in the First Battalion.

I yelled, "Come over here, Bragin!" And just at that moment a shell exploded, catapulting him several metres away.

The Germans' further intentions and their other forward positions were naturally unknown to me. I reckoned that if the Germans got dug in here, then sooner or later they'd find us in this hollow. So as soon as the tanks moved off a little, I decided to search out those who'd survived and go out along the front line at right angles to the area of the German advance to the main road, cross it, and then move east to the forest tract, where I expected to come across two regiments of our division. There were just five of us in the hollow, including second lieutenant Preklonsky, in command of my mortar company. We were stretched out in a thin line, moving through the hollow to the highway. We crawled across a field of rye. Acrid sweat mixed with dust plastered our eyes; we moved almost blindly. Someone on the left side called to us, and two more men jumped out of the rye: the commander of the regimental battery and a soldier carrying a gun. For some reason I asked where our weapons were. He pointed to the soldier's gun. "There."

He told me how they'd managed several salvoes but they had no anti-tank grenades, so the 'tigers' had made mincemeat of their weaponry and mowed down both men and horses. By some kind of miracle he and this soldier had survived.

We moved on. As we were crossing the road we were hit by machine gun fire. Bullets spattered along the asphalt literally between us but didn't hit anyone. We threw ourselves down into a ditch beside the road and crawled into a clump of alders that grew alongside the road—but now we could walk and already felt a bit bolder.

Not long afterwards we went towards a house standing almost directly on the main road. The house was made of stone with beautiful big windows framed with stucco and good solid farm buildings, but the seal of neglect stamped all of them. The yard was overgrown with weeds, burdock, and the remains of fencing. In the yard we spotted a concrete well with a large wheel that looked like a ship's helm. We decided to pop in, have a drink and a wash. And just as we were looking, the door opened and out on to the porch came an old lady of about eighty-five. She was tall and thin with long, tousled grey hair, barefoot; she looked at us with hatred and triumph.

I addressed her, "Old woman, we'd like to have a drink and a wash".

She replied in the purest possible Russian, "Get away from here, you cursed people. Get away, that's final!"

And raising her hands, she added, "There is a God, He exists. You wanted to beat the Germans, you swine! God exists!"

I said to her, "Old woman, for sure we'll be back. We'll win through, you'll see."

"No! You cursed ones will never be in my place—your time's up and you're not going to get any water from me. Get out of my yard!"

The soldier standing beside me had clicked the bolt of his gun, but I stopped him, and on we went without another word. Her curses followed us for a long time. So that is how the land of Lithuania greeted its liberators!

We soon reached the forest. The German tanks were standing about fifty metres from the edge of the forest but for some reason they were not firing. Almost as soon as I got into the forest I met Bazarny, the regimental chief of staff. He looked downcast and miserable, his face was white. He looked at me with unconcealed astonishment as if I were a ghost from another world (which wasn't far from the truth). The first thing I heard from him was, "Surely this time he'll be judged for war crimes by a military tribunal."

He was referring to our chief, Marfenkov, and he told me that the divisional commander had warned Marfenkov that it was highly likely that German tanks were waiting there ahead of our regiment. These tanks were well camouflaged and even aerial reconnaissance hadn't spotted their exact location, but just the same, Marfenkov had ignored that information. He had hoped to get round the tanks somehow and push on ahead, and that's why he had given us that strange order, to move forward in π formation.

Yet even when they fired at us and we had to spend the night in the open field, he still didn't warn us about the danger from tanks. If he had done so we would have dug out narrow anti-tank trenches and that alone would have let us escape such horrendous losses.

As it turned out later the Germans hadn't expected any counter-attacks from our side either. They had got their infantry and artillery across the river and the tanks were intended to give them mobilised cover. Probably the German reconnaissance knew that our tanks and other heavy firing devices had been held up and so this counter-attack by their tanks would be effective.

Sub-lieutenant Bazarny showed me where to find Marfenkov and, having left my soldiers with Senior Lieutenant Preklonski I headed towards the regimental command headquarters, situated in a small clearing. There I saw a battered automobile we'd won from the Germans. It had no windows left, was riddled with bullet holes and its tyres were burst. A group of workmen stood nearby. They all looked absolutely battered and were all obviously in shock. Marfenkov was sitting on the step of the automobile without his forage cap, the clasp of his officer's belt twisted to one side, the holster with his pistol resting on his stomach. He looked like a man who felt thoroughly ashamed of himself, someone who had completely lost the place. I did not feel sorry for him, just sick...

As captain I was supposed to show respect to my commanding officer. But what kind of captain was I without a battalion and what kind of regimental commander was he without a regiment? My battalion and his whole regiment were lying on that field, the field of our shame. I came up to him. He looked up. "Oh, so you're still alive?" He fell silent and then said quietly, "Go and look after your men."

But there were no men left...